At The Root

At The Root

My journey to health and healing

Kimberly Miles

Foreword by Michael Margolis, DDS

Printed in the United States of America
First Printing: 2017
Published by Kimberly Miles Communications, LLC
Visit our website at www.kimberlymiles.com
Library of Congress Control Number: 2016918563
ISBN: 978-1-62747-008-7
Digital ISBN: 978-1-62747-014-8

For my daughters who inspire me
and
who taught me that it is never too late

Acknowledgements

I wish to express my sincere appreciation and gratitude to those pioneers whose vision and contributions to health and dentistry have made the world more beautiful: Dr. Michael Margolis, Dr. Hal A. Huggins, Dr. Weston Price, Dr. Frank Billings, Dr. E.C. Rosenow, Dr. Martin H. Fischer, Dr. Melvin Page, Dr. George E. Meinig, Mr. Walter J. Clifford, Dr. Boyd Haley, Dr. Christopher Hussar, Dr. J.E. Bouquot, Dr. Thomas E. Levy and Dr. Robert Kulacz.

A heartfelt thanks goes to Dr. Daniela Hutyrova who never stopped encouraging my quest for health. To Karen Von Merveldt-Guevara whose expertise and tenacity put me on the path to finding the root cause of my symptoms. I greatly value our friendship. To you both I am eternally grateful.

To Robin Bailey, Michi Nadler, Dr. Steven Johnson, the late Dr. Mark Viafora, William Gajewski, Rinzai, Sarah Tewhey, Hayley Merchant, William Hanrahan, Debbie Crick and Gwenn Langmack for being there when I needed you most. Thank you for your loving support and sharing your gifts.

It took a small village of professionals to support me in my dream of writing and publishing this book. To Tom Bird and his staff: I could not have done this without you!

I would also like to thank Dr. Jeannine Kinney from Oak Creek Small Animal Clinic for her compassion and knowledge and for taking good care of the Wiggs. To my loving companion Mr. Wiggles, a small rescue dog who has been by my side through the latter half of my story and as I wrote this book. Thank you, dear Wiggs, for reminding me that love is always the answer.

Thank you to artist and artisan Ann Allen for crafting my two beautiful heart pendants that became my good-luck charms and continued inspiration.

Last but not least, my thanks to my husband Forrest Davis for his efforts in editing the many renditions of this manuscript. Your red pen inspired me to become a better writer and gave me the courage to find my voice. Thank you for your support.

Foreword

By Dr. Michael Margolis

Do you have unexplained health problems that doctors can't treat — or even worse, tell you it's all in your head? With this book, Kim takes you on her journey that so many others have traveled. Far too many have suffered similar health issues that have torn their lives apart.

Kim excelled in high school, especially in writing and athletics. Upon graduation, she was looking forward to a promising college career in writing. However, this all came to an abrupt stop halfway through college — and she had no idea why. She became unable to write or think the way she could just a few short years earlier. Her college experience fell into the depths of despair, anguish, devastation and disappointment. But why did this happen? What was the underlying reason?

Like thousands of teenagers and students, Kim had her wisdom teeth extracted. That appointment dictated the remainder of Kim's college career — and the start of her personal health decline. It took thirty years for her to realize how much this simple procedure had affected her health.

Although Kim's story is unique to her, it plays out similarly for thousands of patients with unexplained health problems. Kim's health problems increased exponentially, and she saw physician after physician, dentist after dentist. No one could offer her a solution until she met an alternative,

European-trained physician who asked her one key question no one had asked before: "What is your dental history?" Shortly after that, Kim was referred to me for treatment.

Kim has a unique writing style that allows you to travel with her through her journey, but it is also filled with fact and science that far too many are unaware of. This book may be the key for you to start making informed decisions for yourself and for your health.

Kim found her key to good health through the tooth-body connection. Will you?

Michael D. Margolis, DDS
Doctor of Integrative Medicine
My Dentist, PC
Mesa, AZ 85210

Every tooth in a man's head is more valuable than a diamond.

Miguel de Cervantes

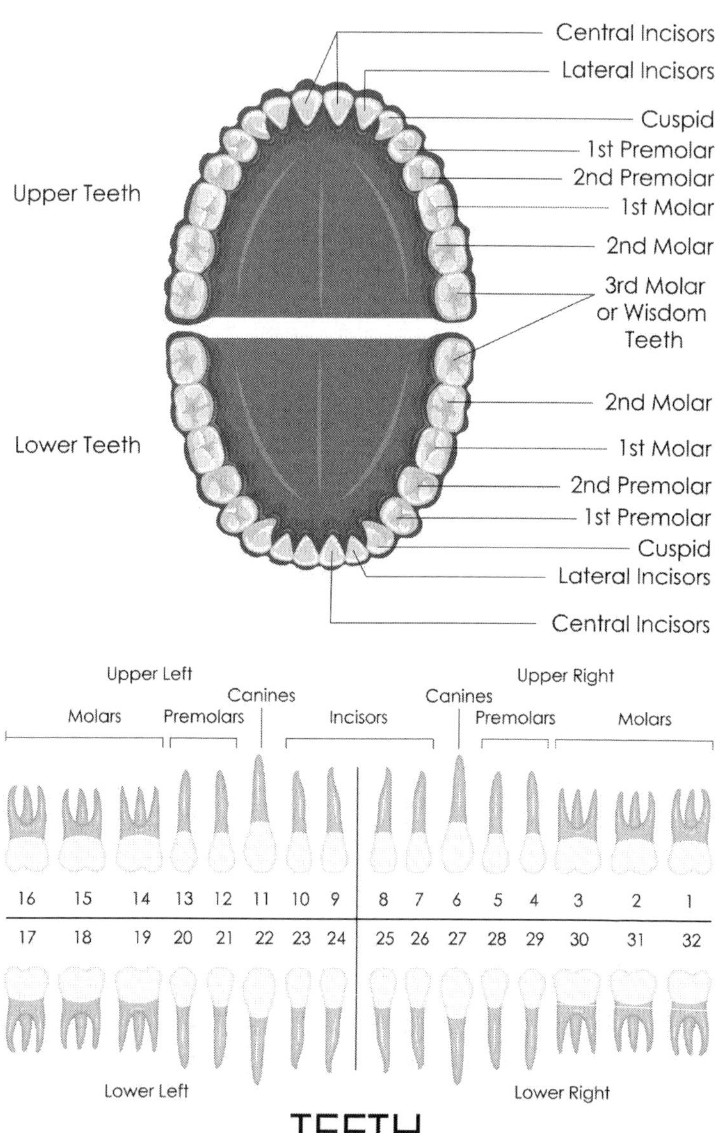

Fig. 1 Anatomy of the mouth

Chapter 1

Boldly go into the great and vast unknown.

Ann Allen

I stood at my bathroom sink, staring into the face in the large mirror before me. My left cheek was slightly swollen and my jawbone tender from the oral surgery I had just gone through that morning. This was the last of my three dental surgeries, which had spanned over a year. On this memorable morning, my dentist had opened up and cleaned out the extraction sites of two of the four wisdom teeth that had been removed when I was twenty. Now that these cavitations were properly treated, my jawbone could fully heal.

At a very basic level, cavitations are voids in the jawbone, or — more simply — holes. More than that, cavitations can be highly toxic holes in the jawbone, because they potentially can harbor chronic infection. For the last thirty years, these cesspools of pathogenic bacteria and their toxic waste had continuously seeped from my jawbone into my body. I believe these toxins burdened my immune system and changed my body's chemistry, causing a myriad of symptoms. The remedy I chose for this problem was to surgically clean out the dead bone tissue and toxic waste from the boney socket so that the area could permanently heal.

For the past thirty years I strove to live a normal, productive and happy life amid mysterious illnesses that were my constant companion. Today's final surgery turned off this fountain of toxins. The majority of my symptoms I had struggled with for so many years were finally gone.

Sighing deeply, I felt the last bit of tension in my shoulders give way. I was tired and sore, but a deep sense of appreciation welled up inside me as soft, gentle chills cascaded through my body. Absent-mindedly, I reached for the heart pendant that rested against my chest. The necklace, a gift from my husband, had accompanied me on all three surgeries. This striking pendant had several small semi-precious stones embedded into the surface, with cutout gold stars, a half moon and engraved shapes. On the back of the heart the artist had engraved, in a feminine script, "Boldly go into the great and vast unknown."[1]

Shifting my gaze, I focused on the view in the mirror out the window that was behind me. I could see the dark-green pine trees in my neighbor's yard. Further beyond I saw the brilliant blue sky, red rocks and rough terrain of Sedona, Arizona. In the mirror I watched two hawks climb in the sky and glide out of view. I had been a pioneer, boldly going into the great and vast unknown to explore the connection between the health of my mouth and the health of my body.

In my many years of going to doctors, with one exception, not once did a doctor look into my mouth to examine my teeth or gums or even to ask me about my dental history. Doctors overlook the mouth when they assess health and well-being. The mouth has been exiled by the medical community and sent off to the exclusive domain of the dentist.[2] I strongly believe that the mouth can become the origin of, or at least a factor in, chronic disease and debilitating illness.

The mouth has a great deal to tell us about our health. It is the gateway to the body and to physical, mental, emotional and spiritual health. The oral cavity, with its seven hundred types of bacteria, is home to approximately ten to fifty billion bacteria, which is the immune system's first line of defense. The oral cavity takes in nourishment and prepares it for digestion and the assimilation of nutrients that keep the body running smoothly.

One of my favorite Greek mythologies illustrates the importance of what goes into our mouth. Zeus and his wife Metis, the Goddess of Prudence who acted as his advisor, were expecting their first child. Zeus worried about the prophecy that foretold the overthrow of his rule by his second child, as Zeus had done to his own father. Zeus's solution was to trick Metis into turning herself into a fly — and then he swallowed her. Their daughter Athena, the Goddess of Wisdom, later sprang from his head as a full-grown woman dressed in armor. As for Metis, the goddess lived inside of Zeus, nurturing and nourishing him with her wise counsel.

Metis symbolically portrays the inner resources of wisdom, insight and clarity that reside within our own body, heart and soul. We have been taught to discount and distrust these critical gifts, which are an important pathway to self-acceptance, self-love and self-care. We all have access to these inner resources, but what we place in our mouth, whether it be food, drink, medications or dental work, influences how well we can hear the authentic voice of our own wise and loving inner counsel. Placing unhealthy things in the mouth affects the body and mind in undesirable ways that distort and turn down the volume of our inner counsel into an inaudible whisper. This ability to connect with our inner counsel — in the form of our heart, gut instincts, knowing or intuition — is critical to the overall quality of our lives. It affects how we think and feel, and whether we can express ourselves authentically. To keep the mouth as healthy as possible is a sacred responsibility, and an act of supreme self-love.

The mouth is a sacred organ. The King James version of the Bible tells us, "For of the abundance of the heart his mouth speaketh" (Luke 6:45): the heart being the channel for gratitude, kindness, forgiveness, resilience, and most of all, the power of love. The mouth is the avenue for the flow of wisdom from our soul. The Bible says, "For I will give you a mouth and wisdom" (Luke 21:15). Through the mouth we express our creativity, ideas, thoughts and emotions. The mouth gives clarity and form to our hopes, dreams and desires. The mouth connects us to family and friends and allows us to share, support, nurture, and pass on the stories and the wisdom of others.

Our culture is full of idioms of the mouth that colorfully describe different concepts. We say:

- "I had a bad taste in my mouth," which means I was left with a bad impression.
- "Being a loud mouth" means not knowing when to be quiet, or talking without thinking.
- "Down in the mouth" is another way to say I am discouraged or sad.
- "Mouth-watering" refers to delicious food.
- "Put your money where your mouth is" means to take action and just not talk about something you believe in.
- "Word of mouth" means to pass information from person to person.

- "Shooting off your mouth" is saying things you should not.
- "Born with a silver spoon in his mouth" means to be born into a wealthy, privileged family.

The mouth may well be the root of all evil, as well as a megaphone that announces our humanity, love and thirst for connection and knowledge. The mouth is a critical instrument of pleasure and pain that shapes and defines us throughout our lives. By what we choose to communicate to others, our lives become a matter of discovery or denial. Despite the importance the mouth plays in our culture, we do not understand the ramifications of placing things into the mouth that have no business being there. We have not figured out that what goes into our mouth affects the overall functioning and health of both the body and the mind.

Through the art of dentistry, many people still have mercury fillings. Others have combinations of dissimilar metals such as copper, titanium, cadmium, beryllium, zinc, nickel and mercury. Dissimilar metals act as a battery to create a "galvanic current." I believe we allow dead, "non-vital" teeth to remain in our midst through a process called root canal treatment. We are taught to believe that anything that is done to the mouth does not affect our overall health.

I have learned a great deal as I sought optimal health these many years. One of my favorite presidents, Ronald Reagan, said "Trust, but verify." I wanted to understand the possible causes behind my symptoms. On this journey, I did my own research and asked hard questions that the medical community could not answer: What is the root cause of my illness or disease? Would the medicine they prescribed give my body what it needed to heal, so that I could permanently resolve the problem? Would the treatment make my body stronger and more resilient?

The medical community could help me manage symptoms, but could not give me solutions. We were speaking in two different languages. Left with no choice, I had to depend upon my own inner resources. As I studied the human body, I found answers in natural health, nutrition and functional medicine. Through research, and trial and error, I tried different supplements, herbs and natural therapies in order to help myself heal. I realized along the way that I often made decisions with my mind but without consulting my heart. This never ended well. Slowly, I learned to ask myself "Is this really best for me?" and "What are the different options I can explore?" and "What would best meet my needs?" I learned to be patient and wait for the answers in order to take inspired action.

The words "decision" and "choice" are used interchangeably, but I now see them as two different steps of the same process. The mind makes decisions. The heart makes choices, through knowing that at this very moment nothing else will do. Choices can only be made after decisions have been decided upon. Decisions take work, research and effort. Decision-making is a process for the mind as it gathers and sifts through information in order to present acceptable options. Once these options are understood, the next step is to make a choice. A choice is a yes or no from the heart that originates from a feeling of what is authentically correct at that moment.

As I used this decision-making model, I observed that joy always followed in the unfolding of the path that I had chosen through my heart's intuition. Along the way, synchronicities surprised me, desires were fulfilled and questions answered. The result has been a profound sense of satisfaction, peace and success. I absolutely know that I have taken the right steps for me to reclaim and assume control of my health and well-being. My results speak for themselves.

After thirty years, my search led to biological dentistry, which solved the majority of my problems and I believe revealed the root causes of my symptoms. I experienced first hand that the answers I sought about my health and life ultimately reside within myself. I strove to live authentically, to have my external world reflect my inner one in which I wanted to live. My decisions and actions flowed from my own inner values and what was meaningful to me, instead of from the status quo of other people and organizations that have their own agendas. I learned not to fear the judgment of others, or even my own. I became free to be in the moment to choose what was most life-giving to me. Living authentically can be a challenge, but it is also a joyful and useful pursuit.

The culture of medicine and dentistry is slowly changing. No longer are the doctor and dentist the authority of knowledge and decision-making. We are beginning to move towards a patient-centered approach where the doctor and patient work as a team. I believe this can empower the patient and result in better outcomes. But this is only a first step of many that must be taken. Patients are responsible to create and live healthy lifestyles and constructively manage stress.

Patients must take responsibility for their health and treatment by doing research, gathering information and asking questions. It is critical to fully understand the benefits and risks of procedures and how they will affect the entire body. Unfortunately, it is up to the patient to search out alternatives or adjunct therapies that support the body during standard medical treatment. Ultimately, patients have the right to access treatments that directly address the root cause of their problems rather than just manage symptoms.

The fact of the matter is that most people do not know anything about their body — the anatomy or physiology or even how it functions. We are at a disadvantage because our bodies do not come with a care and instruction manual. The body is a sacred temple that needs to be treated and viewed as such. We are ready for a paradigm shift about how we view and care for our bodies. Change is inevitable, but there is great resistance because of what we do not know, are afraid of or do not understand.

Today we have incredible access to information, thanks to both the Internet and the many books about others' experiences, expertise and research. The freedom to choose comes with the responsibility to gain clarity. First, we must understand our needs. Second, we must do the research to become educated. Then, we can use that clarity to make inspired choices. Decision-making requires wisdom: the ability to confidently allow the process to unfold before us with options that are most supportive. This is accomplished by the combined guidance of both the heart and the mind.

As I stood looking into my bathroom mirror that afternoon after my last surgery, I felt so appreciative and blessed for the things I had learned and experienced, and for the people I had met. I now value patience. I discovered that I had to live into the answers I sought. Each bit of information I found, and each experience I had, led me to the next discovery and to new ways to help myself. As I looked for different ways to achieve vitality and better health, my search led me through a long and winding maze of education, lifestyle changes, personal growth, experiences, decisions and choices. Over time, I developed a strong sense of what was correct for me and what might work for my body.

I learned to nurture and support my body naturally. I used natural therapies and supplements to help my body rid itself of wastes and toxins, since my body struggled to accomplish this most basic function. Organic whole foods nourished my body's natural ability to heal. Functional tests gave me information about what my body needed, and what it was able or not able to do at that moment. I made my mind an advocate for my own well-being. I stopped listening to my mind criticize, judge or condemn me. I began to choose my thoughts the way I do my friends, allowing in only those that would be supportive and helpful. I chose thoughts that would make me feel good about my life, my choices and myself.

My mantra for those thirty years was "When in doubt, throw it out." I got rid of all kinds of clutter in my life. I sought to reduce the stress on my body, and any stressful situations. I often felt betrayed and thought my body was doing things that were wrong. I now know that my body was doing everything it could to keep me as healthy and safe as possible under the circumstances. I just did not understand the intelligence my body possessed, or the language it used to communicate. It was not until many years later that I was able to "give mouth" to what was ultimately causing the deterioration of my health and vitality — so that I could eradicate it.

Chapter 2

But let no man say what they would or would not do, since we are not judges for ourselves until circumstances call us to act.

Abigail Adams

Two weeks after that final surgery with my biological dentist, I sat on the deck outside my bedroom. The air was crisp and clean. I was surrounded by darkness, but out in the large blanket of the night sky above Sedona, millions of stars quietly twinkled and kept me company. Occasionally a shooting star interrupted the peacefulness as it streaked across the sky. I closed my eyes and made the same wish over and over again on each star. I marveled at the magic and beauty all around me. Out on my deck this evening, anything seemed possible. Life was a gift to be cherished.

Memories flooded back about all I had done over the years to handle my health, and to live as best I could. I started to connect the dots to all the strange health ailments I had experienced over the past thirty years. Before my visit to a biological dentist, I had never heard of cavitations, those infected, stagnant holes in the jawbone. I pictured these cavitations as toxic fountains in my extracted wisdom teeth and two root canals. I felt that my immune system was not only being accosted daily by waste from my own body and the environment, but it also had to deal with an abundant, never-ending array of toxins generated from my mouth. I thought that was why my diets, cleanses and all the therapies and modalities I worked with over the years never gave me results. Everything I did certainly helped to take the edge off, but because the "root cause" was not addressed and removed, my symptoms always came back, and even worsened over time. The answer to my health problems indeed had its origins in my mouth.

Questions that had no answers poured through my mind. I wondered how my life would have unfolded had I not been so sick for these many years. Who would I have been if only there had been biological dentists to remove my wisdom teeth when I was twenty? Where would I be? Strong emotions of sorrow and grief began to surface. I allowed myself to feel and observe them. My body shivered in order to release these emotions one by one. I focused on my breath as I slowly inhaled and exhaled to the rhythm of the twinkling stars.

As I watched the expansive night sky, I experienced sadness, then anger, and finally a sense of relief. I felt sadness for all the lost possibilities and time, anger for having had my health and well-being compromised. I felt relief because this chapter of my life had come to an end. Tears of joy and anticipation for a healthier future quietly rolled down my checks. I embraced my legs in my arms and placed my chin on my knees. I gave myself a much-needed hug as the feeling of appreciation welled up in me. I had entered another transitional phase in my life, which I welcomed. The end of health problems and lack of well-being had come to a close; a new adventure of healing was about to begin. I was curious to see what my body would do now and what it could achieve.

Being sick is a lonely venture. No one could really understand what I went through and its impact on me. Well-meaning people told me that my problems were not that bad, and that I should give up my search and accept the diagnoses my doctors gave me. After all, doctors are the authorities. But I could not ignore the conviction that there was a solution that would bring my body back to optimal health, and that I would find it. This conviction resonated through every bone in my body. It was an absolute knowing that transcended belief. I always knew the answer was out there, waiting for me to find it.

The heart pendant that hung around my neck was a constant reminder that I could not rely solely on the accepted authority of other people and institutions. "Boldly go into the great and vast unknown," inscribed in a feminine script, reminded me that I had entered territory for which I had no point of reference. I had to become more heart-felt, to go inside myself, and to trust my own inner authority. I had to believe in myself. I learned to remain open, to be receptive and to be mindful of the unconditional love that guided me throughout my journey.

As I went through my surgeries, there were a handful of people who supported me, but many of my friends and family did not share my enthusiasm. They thought I had lost my mind. They consulted their dentists and doctors about my "cavitations" and root canals. They were told that what I planned to do was unnecessary, and that cavitations are not a problem in the mouth. My dental work just could not have any connection to my overall health. To them, my intended course of action was unorthodox.

Dr. Mark Breiner, in his book *Whole Body Dentistry,* mentions that dentists are not taught about cavitations in dental school even though they are referred to in dental pathology.[3] I discovered through my experience that I had cavitations, which were silent lesions, in my jawbone. I learned that cavitations are quite common, often found in the sockets of extracted teeth and root canals. "All cavitations are toxic. If they were not toxic, the jawbone would have healed," according to scientist Dr. Boyd Haley who has studied these toxins.[4] Cavitation surgeries are then the only way for healing of the jawbone to occur and can offer improved health to patients.

Through my personal experience, I believe that cavitation surgeries play a large supporting role in removing a portion of the overall toxic load in the body — at least the portion that originates from the mouth. I realized that my cavitation surgeries did not heal my body any more than a dentist or doctor does, but they helped to reduce the overall burden on my immune system so that my body could do its job better and heal. I have always believed that the body does its best to find its own way back to health and well-being.

The professionals who treat cavitations and root canals have honed their skills and have developed ways to identify these unwanted conditions. Cavitations can be difficult to detect on traditional x-rays, especially if the dentist has not been trained.[5] Biological dentists are pioneers who are slowly changing the status quo. These remarkable individuals were trained as conventional dentists, but had profound experiences (either for themselves or with their patients) that challenged their beliefs and the way they practice dentistry. Biological dentists endure criticism and worse from dental institutions and state dental boards. Insurance does not cover much of their work at all. This makes biological dentistry financially out of reach for many people.

I shook my head and shrugged my shoulders. I could have listened to everyone else's opinions when I told them I was working with a biological dentist. My family and friends meant well. I understood that they needed to be in their own comfort zones. Beliefs are powerful things. When faced with the most compelling evidence that contradicts what is believed or what has been taught, it is human nature to do everything possible to protect those thoughts and those ways of doing things. I wanted to believe that the medical and dental institutions — and the doctors and dentists whom I respected — were the authorities, the ones who would always know what was best for me. Certainly their opinions, protocols and research were a starting point. But ultimately I needed to take responsibility for myself. I needed to follow the voice of my own inner authority.

I respected my friends' and family's opinions and beliefs, but they were not me and they had not experienced life the way I had. It was not worth trying to explain anything to them. They would not be able to see my point of view. It was better just to agree to disagree and move on. I would let the results speak for themselves. I was glad to have stood my ground and gone ahead with the three surgeries that allowed me to reclaim my health, my vitality and my well-being. The biggest gift of all is that my life has been given back to me. I experienced many positive outcomes from my cavitation surgeries. When all else failed, I trusted my heart and gut instincts. I realized that I am the best authority for both my health and my life.

I touched the heart pendant that hung around my neck as I sat on my deck. I gazed up at the star-studded night sky and smiled softly to myself. Throughout my journey I never lost hope, although at times it would have been easier to do so. I had faith that everything would somehow work out. I thought about all the wonderful people I had met and all the adventures I'd had along the way. My life had not turned out the way I had imagined when I was growing up. Woody Allen was right when he said, "If you want to make God laugh, tell him about your plans."

A warm breeze began to stir. My neighbor's pine trees swayed and made a rustling noise. I spotted another shooting star as it made its way across the sky. I took a deep breath and repeated the same wish I had made earlier as the star quickly disappeared. My wish was more of a prayer of thanksgiving. "Thank you for my body, my mouth, my health and my bright future."

The night air hummed with the sound of insects. As I looked out across the yard, I heard a faint fluttering noise. I squinted my eyes and saw the dark outlines of three small bats. They seemed to dance through the night sky as they moved off towards my orchard. Bats, known as "guardians of the night," symbolize rebirth. I could not think of a more appropriate omen as I began my new life. Now I could truly imagine a happy and healthy future. But first, tonight I would remember and give one more nod to the past.

Chapter 3

When health is absent, wisdom cannot reveal itself, art cannot become manifest, strength cannot be exerted, wealth is useless, and reason is powerless.

Herophiles 300 B.C.

Growing up, I had generally experienced good health. Sure I had my share of runny noses, upset stomachs and scraped knees, but I was usually energetic, athletic, creative and optimistic about life. Health, fitness and well-being were important to my family. I came to value the importance of a healthy lifestyle: good nutrition, proper sleep, exercise and sportsmanship. Education was equally emphasized: "a sound mind in a sound body," my grandfather repeatedly told my sister and me.

My grandfather, Pop-Pop, was a gregarious, tall and handsome man with a gleam in his eye, who greatly valued education. I listened carefully to the conversations at the weekly Sunday night dinner table when we visited my grandparents because I always learned something new. Even though the prevailing rule was "children are seen but not heard," Pop-Pop always welcomed my questions about economics, politics, history, human nature, art and literature. In fact, he encouraged them. He was the smartest and wisest person I knew. I have never forgotten what my grandfather wrote in my autograph book when I was in second grade,

"Good, better, best, never let it rest, until your good is your better and your better is your best."

I had been a good student, curious about everything. I always wanted to better myself. There was no doubt in my mind that I would attend college and go on to graduate school. College was a big adventure for me. In my freshman year, I presented my advisor with a highlighted course catalogue of the classes that I thought looked interesting. I was so excited about all the different course offerings in psychology, philosophy, sociology, history, human development, neuroscience, art history, English, writing and art. I wanted to take everything. My advisor laughed and exclaimed that if I took all those courses, I would never graduate! I found it fun to learn new things and to challenge myself. I also enjoyed meeting and making new friends. At college, I was in my element.

Things began to change after spring break of my junior year, following the extraction of my four wisdom teeth. I felt "off" and could not figure out why. It puzzled me. It never occurred to me that there could be a connection between my mouth and my health. My health slowly began to fail. I caught and then had trouble recovering from what seemed to be every cold and flu that went around campus. By the end of the semester I noticed other changes. I struggled with my schoolwork; it became difficult to focus. I was embarrassed and horrified by my new memory problems. Trying to retain information and study for exams became a stressful challenge.

I was exhausted. Because I was so tired all the time, I had to save my energy for schoolwork. I cut out extracurricular activities like tennis, guitar and volunteer work. I no longer had the energy to go out with friends. Socializing became difficult, and I could not connect with people in the genuine way I had in the past. The best description is that my life became "muted" or blurry." I felt cut off and separated from the hustle and bustle of campus life. I spent much time alone, isolated in my small room. I would sit at my desk, books unopened, and listen to the laughter and animated conversations of my fellow students. I felt lonely and left behind as my friends got busy with their activities and their lives. I tried to carry on as if nothing was wrong.

My bed was positioned across from my desk and bookshelf. That was where I spent most of my time when I was not in class or studying. I took several brief naps each day. I would go to bed early but the rest that I got was never enough. I longed for the deep, restful sleep I'd experienced growing up. As I stretched out on my bed, I would look up at a large framed poster that my father had given me when I declared my art history major. The picture on the poster was of a medium-sized, dark-brown wooden shadow box by the twentieth-century American artist Joseph Cornell. He was known for his intricate, enigmatic, elaborate glass-front boxes that contained collage-like assemblages made from pages of books, found objects and bric-a-brac from second-hand stores. (Fig. 2)

The image in the shadow box was one of many themes that Cornell displayed in his work: a famous portrait from the sixteenth century of the Medici Princess, Bia. Framing her cropped image were square columns collaged with the floor plans of her parents' palace in Florence, Italy. Spirals made of thin and delicate strips of metal adorned the upper hand corners of the elegant box. On either side were messily stacked blocks, covered with either her portrait or that of a boy. There were other blocks, too, with stars and numbers on them. The columns stood on a glass shelf, the width of the box.

Fig. 2 "Bia." A Medici Princess, c.1948 (3D object), Cornell, Joseph (1903 -1972)/Private Collection/Bridgeman Images. Used with Permission.

Below was a row of more children's blocks collaged with sepia-colored images of birds, plants, a sundial and a ladder. A slightly opened drawer in the bottom of the box refused to reveal its contents. I would try to imagine what the drawer could possibly hold. All of these common objects together as a whole paid homage to Bia's brief life, which was cut short by a fever when she was only six.

Bia, the little princess, mesmerized me. Drawn over her image was a vertical dark line that visually divided that section of the box into two equal halves. The artist had also drawn three horizontal lines: one below her eyebrows, another through her pupils, and the third above the bottom section of her nose. Another horizontal line ran over her fingers and through the top third of a small red ball. My eyes continually traced over the lines that made Bia seem less accessible to me. I spent so much time looking at that poster that I joked to my friends that Bia was my roommate.

Even though I was sick and tired, I greeted my senior year with great enthusiasm. I was excited that I would finally get to take a creative writing course. As long as I could remember, I had a passion for writing. In junior high school I wrote stories and illustrated them for fun. My English teacher would sometimes let me read them aloud to the class. The creative writing course required that I submit a current writing sample to the teacher. I had not written anything since sophomore year so I submitted a short story I had written back then. Much to my dismay, I had developed writer's block, but I thought that being surrounded by other budding writers would be inspirational.

During class, I sat and stared at the blank sheets in front of me. Ideas and words would not come. I felt frustrated because the brain fog I was experiencing made me tire easily and become unfocused. It was difficult to find the right words. My creativity and clarity evaporated. My childhood dream to become an author no longer seemed possible. The final blow came when the teacher called me into her office. She told me that the quality of my work was not up to the caliber of the short story I had submitted. She looked at me intently and was quiet for a moment. As she looked down at the floor and cleared her throat, she quietly suggested that I withdraw from the course.

I left her office feeling totally numb. I went directly back to my dorm room and lay on the bed. I looked up at Bia, who was now blurry through the tears that stung my cheeks. I glanced at her left hand (her right hand was hidden behind the column) and then at the red ball, which was carefully positioned on the shelf in the far corner, out of her reach. Bia was denied her toy, but for me the red ball took on a different significance. It symbolized my creativity, my clarity and my vitality, all of which were now out of *my* reach. Bia's toy blocks were piled up on either side of her, yet she could neither see them nor play with them. I, too, felt that the building blocks of my life were there, but for some unknown reason, were no longer available to me. Bia was trapped in her box, but I was trapped in my body. What had happened to my health? As I stared off into space I had a thought: perhaps the solution, the answer to my question, resided metaphorically in that partially opened drawer. If the answer was in there, I could not yet see it. If the answer was there, I was determined to find it.

Chapter 4

It does not matter how slow you go as long as you do not stop.

Confucius

Despite the tiredness and brain fog, I was somehow able to maintain my grades. I was accepted to a graduate program in Washington, D.C. When I was in high school, my grandmother had taken me to our nation's capital on one of our many spring-break trips. I fell in love with this beautiful city, with all its hustle and bustle. It had wonderful things to offer: museums, galleries and monuments. I decided that one day, when I grew up, I would live there. Never forgetting that intention, I was excited to finally move there. I was hopeful that the change of scenery would do me good. But shortly after I got settled and started school, my appetite began to dwindle. I was stricken with abdominal pains that made me double over. The bloating became worse and I lost a lot of weight. The doctor decided I had developed food allergies, due to the fact that my face and neck would swell without warning. Itchy skin rashes would often appear after I ate. There was no discernible pattern as to what foods caused these allergic reactions. I would remove what I thought was the offending food from my diet, but it did not seem to matter. As a result, there was almost nothing that I thought I could eat. Mealtime became stressful.

The pleasure of eating that I had always enjoyed completely disappeared. In desperation I began to eat jars of baby food because I thought that might stop the swelling and discomfort, but it did not. The doctor put me on prednisone, an immune-suppressant steroid drug, to control the swelling and inflammation. I did not take the medicine for long, because it made me feel awful and sick to my stomach. It also did not help. I felt discouraged and overwhelmed. What was left of my self-confidence started to dwindle.

At night I would lie awake listening to the traffic out on the avenue, and wonder if this was what the rest of my life would be like. I had no real direction or purpose. I knew there had to be something more, but what? I knew that something was not right, that there was more to life than my constant struggle to get through the day. I wanted my energy and stamina back. I wanted to experience the best that life had to offer. I wanted to know myself more deeply and discover what I was capable of achieving. I wanted to become the best person I could be. I had lost my sparkle and no longer enjoyed life. I knew that life could and should be better.

During my second year of graduate school, I met my first husband through a graduate internship. The relationship took a lot of my focus off my health, which actually helped me feel a little bit better. But by the time we married the following year, my schedule had become harder to navigate due to my exhaustion, and the demands of graduate school, a husband and a part-time job.

The doctors that I went to during those years in hopes of figuring out what was wrong had no answers. The only thing for certain was that my list of symptoms had become longer. I had a sinking feeling deep inside of me that made me feel afraid and alone. I was out of control and did not know what to do. My ill health had totally disrupted my life. My family and my doctors were baffled as well. They told me that I was probably stressed out and needed to learn to relax. One doctor said it was most likely PMS. Another doctor thought I looked healthy enough to him. He suggested that perhaps I was overreacting — and it was likely that my health issues were all in my head. From a certain point of view he was correct! It never dawned on the doctors (or me) that the four wisdom teeth that had been extracted during my junior year of college were a potential factor in my health issues.

The stress of the continuous stream of toxicity drowned out the voice of my body and heart, and its intuitive guidance. My mind shouted "What's wrong with you?" "Pull yourself together!" "Obviously you just are not good enough, smart enough, strong enough," and on and on.

Seven years into my marriage, I became pregnant with my first daughter. I was overjoyed! Being pregnant had given me a reason to be tired and not feel well. I actually felt relieved. But after the birth of my daughter, I suffered from postpartum depression. I threw myself into caring for my beautiful baby; she was my joy. In my postpartum depressed state I had even less energy than I'd had before. I felt like I was drowning in a sea of exhaustion. Besides taking care of my baby, I had no energy left to perform basic tasks like making dinner or doing laundry. I depended heavily on my husband for help. I felt further disconnected from the world, and from other people. It was as if someone had put blinders on me. I slipped into a great abyss, and desperately looked for a magic bullet to pull me out.

The postpartum depression lifted when I became pregnant with my second daughter. I loved being a mom and looked forward to raising my two girls. Two weeks before the birth of my second daughter, however, I came down with pneumonia, a common occurrence for me since college. A few days after I finished the course of antibiotics, my second daughter was born. Wiped out at this point, I literally felt as though my body had broken up into pieces.

I was so physically and mentally exhausted I could not think straight. I was unable to make the simplest decision, which greatly annoyed my husband. I felt very little motivation to get things done. Doing anything besides taking care of the girls took a great deal of effort. My house was a mess, I was disheveled and I had a room piled high with half-started projects that I'd never had the energy to finish. Was this what I wanted to model for my children? It was not. What I wanted my girls to see was a happy, creative, productive, energetic, vibrant and healthy woman.

Each afternoon I looked forward to a nap with the girls. I had already put them to bed when I caught my image in the hallway mirror. I stopped and studied my face. I took a good, hard look and realized that I did not like the person staring back at me. She was a stranger. I shook my head in frustration and looked into the eyes of the face that stared back at me. For the first time in many years, I had a flash of insight into my life. I saw myself clearly: a thirty-something, stressed-out woman who was sick and tired of being sick and tired. I did not know who I was anymore. I had lost my footing. A feeling of dread moved through my chest and made me shiver.

I intuitively knew that in order for me to be authentic, my inner world — the world of my emotions, my thoughts and my body — had to match the outer world of my actions and my daily reality.

My life was not a reflection of the woman I knew myself to be: strong, self-reliant, creative, vibrant and authentic. Standing there in front of the mirror, I found myself living in a world not of my own creation — or liking. I was in survival mode most of the time, managing my health and just getting by. I realized I was making decisions based on the fear of being cast aside, deemed broken and not good enough by my own mind and by others. I was afraid of drowning, of being swallowed up into the abyss of irrelevance and weakness. I felt like a failure. What had happened to my potential? This was supposed to be one of the happiest times of my life. I knew that I was out of balance, but I also knew I lacked the information I needed. Clearly, some of the puzzle pieces were missing.

Unbeknownst to me, what was left of my marriage was quickly disintegrating. I was too busy with the girls and too preoccupied with my health to notice. I was heartbroken when I finally realized that my marriage was over. One afternoon, while the girls played, I was busily folding the laundry. I would give them each a sock and shirt to fold, which neither one was capable of doing really well. It did not matter, because we had a good time together as we giggled and listened to Barney, the purple dinosaur, sing silly songs.

There were several items in the pile that belonged to my husband. We had always purchased his clothing together. But this afternoon, I picked up a cotton sweater that I did not recognize. My husband had bought this without me. To make matters worse, I did not even notice that he had obviously worn it. Suddenly it dawned on me that my husband was no longer spending much time at home. He and I had stopped talking. We had become strangers, existing in the same house. I examined the cable-knit pattern that added texture to the sea of soft, dark-blue yarn. I held the sweater up as if to wait for it to offer an explanation, but it was silent. Yet this simple purchase he had made without me said volumes. It served as a symbol of a relationship gone awry. Standing there holding the sweater, I felt as if someone had taken a sledgehammer to my heart. At that moment, the fog temporarily lifted. I clearly understood that our marriage had been over for at least the past five years, and that nobody had bothered to tell me.

The next several months were a blur to me. I tried to recount the events as I stood on the bank of the Hudson River in Tarrytown, New York. The girls and I had driven up alone for a family wedding. A mile away, the church I had been married in twelve years earlier lay quietly empty. It was an early, gray Saturday morning. My beloved river had been the backdrop to my childhood. The Hudson was where I'd enjoyed picnics with my friends, and where I'd received my first kiss. I would find refuge by the river whenever I needed peace and solitude.

Today was no different. As an adult with two young children, I now came to seek both freedom and answers. The failure of my marriage acted as a great catalyst. I became angry; I wanted to know what had happened to me, and why. I demanded to know the root cause of my health issues. I wanted to know why so many things had gone wrong. Friends would tell me I was in the process of learning a "life lesson." Throughout life there is much to learn, and wisdom to gain, through experience. Challenges, problems and trauma are part of being human. I never saw these as a punishment or a "life lesson" that I was being forced to learn on a list of things to be checked off.

As I stood there in the green grass on the bank of the Hudson, I felt strangely empowered and hopeful. I had worked diligently to try to save my marriage, but it was just not possible. I was now on a path of no return, and I meant to make a grand gesture with the help of my beloved river. The girls stood quietly by my side, curious to see what I was about to do. I think, for an instant, they were in as much awe of the river as I had been. My right hand shook as I tightly clutched my gold wedding ring; I opened my hand to reveal an imprint of it on my palm. As I took a deep breath, I noticed the sunlit bank on the other side of the river. I thought how wonderful it would be to feel the warmth of the sun on my face. At that moment the wind picked up, and the dark-blue colored water became choppy with small whitecaps.

I stood firmly in the grass and addressed the wind. I asked for love, for happiness, for health, for guidance and for wisdom. I knew in my heart that I was put here on this planet Earth to love life, and to experience the best that it had to offer. I was here to live joyfully and to become the best person I could be. It was time to release the past, and to forgive myself for the things I could not control.

I took a deep breath. Then, with all my heart and soul, and with my entire being, I lifted my arm and threw my wedding ring as far and as hard as I could. The girls screamed in excitement, jumping up and down as we watched the ring catapult up into the air and begin its descent downward as if in slow motion. The wind began to chase away the clouds. The sunlight from the opposite riverbank rushed out over the Hudson. At that very instant, the sun kissed my ring and flashed out a glowing light as the gold band gently hit the waves. The ring seemed to hesitate before it quickly disappeared beneath the surface of the water. As it sank to the bottom, the girls and I stood bathed in a bright light on the riverbank.

It was over.

Chapter 5

The most courageous act is still to think for yourself. Aloud.

Coco Chanel

The stress of the divorce took a further toll on my health. I woke up morning after morning with unexplained muscle pain; feeling groggy, exhausted and emotionally raw. Sometimes I wished that I would wake up to discover that my life had just been a bad dream.

As things settled down, I decided to get some answers about my health. I saw different doctors but they had no concrete answers for why I had so many problems. Several of the doctors sent me away explaining it was probably stress. Some suggested I could try anti-depressants, histamines or other drugs, but I knew that those would not solve anything for me. I knew my body did not have a "drug deficiency." I kept searching. I found one doctor who listened carefully to my list of symptoms: fatigue bordering on extreme exhaustion, loss of short-term memory and concentration, enlarged lymph nodes in my neck, unexplained muscle pain, stiffness and swelling, un-refreshing sleep, weight loss, PMS and a slew of respiratory illnesses. He suggested that many of these symptoms sounded like chronic fatigue syndrome (CFS).

That explained why my immune system was compromised and why I was always sick. I wanted to know what the root cause of CFS was, so I could understand what had happened in my body and fix the problem permanently. When I asked the doctor what caused CFS, he said that the cause was unknown and it still is a mystery to researchers today. But at least I now had a name for my health issues. I felt relieved; I was not crazy or a hypochondriac. The doctor told me there was no cure, but he suggested that I make as many healthy lifestyle changes as I could.

An old friend of mine gave me a book, and a set of cassette tapes, entitled *You Can Heal Your Life* by Louise Hay. I listened to those tapes until they wore out. I was interested to hear Louise Hay speak so openly about "loving the self." It was a concept, which up until that point, I had never given any thought to. The idea intrigued me that I could influence "dis-ease" in my body by choosing healthy thought patterns and beliefs about myself, which, in turn, would lower my overall stress level.

I could clearly see that the unkind and negative thoughts I'd had about myself and my body had been creating stressful static in the background of my daily life. I tried to be kinder and gentler with myself. Louise Hay's work reminded me to take responsibility for my thoughts and my life. If I could focus on loving myself more consistently, I reasoned, I could better manage my health and my life. I felt hopeful for the first time in a long time. I wanted to get to know the "true me" who lived behind my tiredness and symptoms. Louise Hay's work was a turning point for me. I felt empowered by everything I learned.

I decided to take some classes to meet new people. I learned how to meditate and do self-hypnosis, as well as other stress-management techniques. I took classes in personal growth to develop my visionary and creative side. I also became interested in nutrition, physiology, biology, anatomy and the mind-body connection. I wanted to learn more about nutrition and supplements. A friend bought me a juicer, and I started to make more changes to my diet. I actually felt a little less tired. I started to develop a greater sense of self-worth and self-confidence.

In my search for wellness, I learned that our bodies are genetically encoded for health and survival. The body knows and recognizes vitality — this is its normal state. The body's amazing ability to adapt to different circumstances is because of this genetic code. Everything the body does is done to survive and protect itself. Anything done to or placed into the body affects the entire organism. This adaptation, meaning a functional change to meet the new demands of the body's inner environment, is often what we refer to as disease, illness and symptoms. Many factors can potentially create disease and evoke a change in the body's chemistry. These risk factors include stress, genetic inheritance, weaknesses in the body, environmental toxins, pathogenic bacteria and viruses, lifestyle choices, unhealthy diet and poorly tolerated pharmaceuticals. What I realized was that disease and illness is a cumulative process, created by a combination of many factors.

In search of more answers, I studied stress management, nutrition and natural health. I knew that my body could heal itself. I marveled at the body's ability to make repairs, to rid itself of waste and to rejuvenate itself. I found comfort in the knowledge that my body actually produces new skin every thirty days, that the mucosa lining of my digestive tract regenerates every five days and that several million red blood cells are replaced in the circulatory system every second. Of course, the catch here is that the body needs the proper raw materials and the correct information from its DNA. Any functional impairment also alters the body's blueprint for health and vitality.

I thought about my CFS diagnosis. What if there was really no such thing as disease and illness? What if nothing had really gone wrong? What if the symptoms I experienced had resulted from the way my body adapted? What if the symptoms were a form of communication in a language I did not yet understand? What if I began to look at the things that were going on in my body not as wrong and incorrect, but as a way of compensating for something — but what? What could affect the inner environment of my body, forcing it to make these changes? If I could just figure out the root cause that made my body behave in a way that I did not like, I could then make the necessary corrections. This simplistic explanation made the most sense to me. I believed in my body's resiliency, in its ability to return to vibrant health and wellness.

The most overlooked relationship we have is with our own body. There is constant communication, whether we are aware of it or not. We communicate to our body through our lifestyle, what we place into our mouths, how we move and exercise, how we deal with stress and emotions, our thoughts and our beliefs, our behaviors and experiences. The body always listens and responds. In the best-case scenario, the body responds with energy, stamina, clarity and a good mood when it is given enough sleep, the nutrients it needs and proper hydration. The body answers with exhaustion, indigestion, aches and pains and a bad mood when it receives abuse in the form of lack of sleep, poor nutrition, dehydration and unrelenting stress. The body's responses are normal and natural under the circumstances in which it finds itself. If we like the results we experience, we call it healthy. If we do not like the results, we call it illness and disease.

My point is that it is possible to change the conversation so that the body can respond differently. The issue here is that in our lifetime we have initiated so many "conversations" (most of which we are not even aware of) that our body must respond to multiple inputs all the time. The challenge is to untangle all these factors and understand what each one means.

The language of healing is often misunderstood. In natural health, illness serves a specific purpose in that it protects the body. For example, mucus is one of the body's mechanisms to release toxic waste; this release often takes the form of a cold. When the inner environment becomes compromised for any reason, the body is challenged and has to prioritize its functions. The body then speaks to us in the symptoms that result. The body in its infinite wisdom constantly seeks homeostasis, that is, balance between its many parts and functions.

The doctors I consulted had no answers on how to specifically support my body so that my symptoms would no longer be needed. They could only offer different medications to manage my symptoms. I was not interested in managing symptoms. With the new understanding of my body, symptom management was akin to a bandage placed over the dashboard light in my car that was letting me know that something was wrong. My goal was to get to the root causes of my issues, and to help correct them, in whatever manner made sense to my body.

More than anything, I wanted to experience the vitality that I felt was my birthright. Stewardship of my health became a priority as I partnered with my body. My interest in health and vitality grew into the need to take inspired action that supported the freedom of the overall function and movement of my body and mind. I felt hopeful that I would be able to decipher the messages my body would send in order to support its healing process. I had faith, and trusted that I would somehow be led to the correct people, places and information I needed.

Chapter 6

Go West, young man, go West and grow with the country.

Horace Greeley

I loved my life in Washington, D.C., the city in which I had lived for nearly twenty years. I attended graduate school there. I met my first husband and had my two daughters there. I belonged to volunteer organizations and play groups for the girls, and we participated in an assortment of activities from ballet lessons to art classes. I had made many good friends whom I cherished. I had taken classes and earned many certifications that grew into a successful nutrition, personal-growth and stress-management consulting business. I was on radio and local cable TV. I enjoyed the status as a favorite speaker at corporate and government health fairs. I served on health panels, lectured and offered an array of popular workshops. I had just released my first guided-relaxation CD, *The Art of Letting Go*. The girls and I took pleasure in our activities and friends. I enjoyed my life in Washington, D.C. despite my many health issues. But signs began to appear that the next chapter of my life belonged elsewhere.

Before the school's winter break, the admissions director informed me that they could not offer a scholarship for my girls to attend kindergarten and first grade the following year.

Within the week, my landlord mentioned to me that there would be a substantial increase in my rent. Then, a driver ran a red light and broadsided my car. Even though there were many pedestrians in the vicinity, no one stopped to help. Another catalyst was that 9/11 had recently occurred. The accumulation of these events made me feel that it was time to leave. I wanted to settle in a new place with a better quality of life in which to raise the girls and improve my health.

On New Year's Eve, as I surfed the Internet, I found a charter school in Sedona, Arizona that emphasized creativity, community and mastery of basic skills. I had visited Sedona as a teenager and found the area beautiful, with its looming red-rock landscape, canyons and pine forests, the meandering Oak Creek, a mild climate and friendly people. Sedona had a "soul-nourishing" feel to it; I felt drawn to the area. Even though I felt a positive sense of adventure about Sedona, I wondered if I should stay in my beloved D.C.

Shortly after school started up again after the holiday break, I mulled the pros and cons of moving to Sedona and got nowhere. My mind asked:

- "Is it really a good idea to leave behind the life that the girls and I have built in Washington?"
- "What about my business, my friends, the girls' father and the girls' activities?"
- "What is waiting for us in Sedona?"
- "Why Sedona?"
- "Will we like it there?"
- "Will the move improve my health?"

Over the next month, as I pondered all these questions, I was no closer to making a choice. Then one morning, my answer came through the mail slot. On the floor lay a catalogue with big, bold letters at the top. It read "Courage to Change."

Over spring break, the girls and I visited Sedona. There was something very magical about the town. The awe-inspiring rugged landscape of red rocks, canyons and desert, along with Sedona's spiritual atmosphere, made me feel that anything was possible. I enrolled the girls in school for the following year and purchased a house just outside of Sedona. At the end of the school year, the girls and I drove cross-country. We took a leap of faith. We left behind friends, my growing business and a life that had not entirely worked. I was not sure of what I was looking for, but I knew that Sedona was our next stop. I grew hopeful as the days of driving went by and the scenery changed. By the time we reached the Gateway Arch, built as a monument to westward expansion in St. Louis, Missouri, I decided that Sedona would bring new opportunities and help me regain my health. By the time we reached the desert landscape of Santa Fe, New Mexico, I was ready and excited to build a new life. So, when we finally reached our new home, I was not prepared for my life to completely fall apart.

The move had been stressful on my body. Several days after we had arrived in the Sedona area, I fainted and fell, and broke an incisor tooth that pushed both front teeth out of alignment. I was devastated. A dentist my neighbor recommended temporarily glued back on the piece of tooth that had broken off. My hope was to be able to nurse the remaining part of that tooth and the other badly damaged front tooth back to health. The trauma was too great, though, and my body too stressed; both teeth died over time. The dentist urged me to "save the teeth" by having root canal procedures. I felt so overwhelmed that I put off doing anything until we were settled into our new life.

The same nightmares I'd had as a child of losing my teeth became a nightly occurrence. How they went missing, I do not know. Sometimes my teeth would begin to fall out, or just disappear. I would run around and scream "My teeth!" and wake up with a start — upset and badly shaken. My heart pounded in my throat. A dream of losing teeth is common in times of increased stress. This dream can signify a period of renewal and rebirth, or the anxiety and uncertainty during a time of transition. I certainly was in transition — that in-between place of a "no-man's land" where my old life was ending as I attempted to make new beginnings. Feeling uncomfortable and impatient, I tried to force my way through the chaos between the two, since both were happening at once.

I felt rather directionless and lost. Not knowing anyone, or knowing my way around the area, amplified my feelings. I did not know what to expect when I arrived, but I certainly did not expect this. My two dying teeth symbolized the deeper changes I was being asked to make in my life. I had uprooted my family to move to Sedona. While I never questioned my decision, my high hopes for improved health — and how I imagined that my new life would look — crashed down around me. I desperately wanted a "happily ever after," and for all my issues to magically disappear, but Sedona had no tooth fairy to wave her magic wand. I would have to figure this out on my own. My main focus was to give my daughters the best life possible.

As we continued to unpack and settle into our new home, I became dismayed by more health problems. I experienced raised red and angry rashes on my legs and torso that sometimes oozed. My digestive problems worsened as I doubled over in pain and clutched my stomach; my food remained undigested. My body moved between constipation and diarrhea. I started to slowly lose what energy I had, and that familiar postpartum grey haze I had experienced with the birth of my daughters returned. Interestingly, I had to return to wearing reading glasses. After I'd had my mercury fillings removed in Washington, D.C., I no longer needed them. I wanted to ignore what was going on in my body and pretend it was not happening. But my health problems were growing too large to ignore. I became terrified, concerned that I would not be able to function enough even to drive my daughters back and forth to their school.

At the end of the second month in my new home, my breathing became labored and difficult. I thought it might be the altitude. One Saturday morning, after I had collapsed onto the floor of the local library, I learned at the Urgent Care center that I had bacterial pneumonia. I refused to go to the hospital. The doctor agreed to let me stay at home. With my health spiraling downwards, I went into survival mode. I could no longer care for my daughters or myself. I became too sick to do much of anything but sleep. I could no longer control my bladder and had to wear adult diapers. I did not understand what was happening to me. My body seemed to be shutting down. Helplessly, I just watched and waited.

While lying in bed in my new house in Arizona, I thought about the inspirational story I'd read to my daughters, entitled *Miss Rumphius,* by Barbara Cooney. As a young girl, Alice Rumphius has two goals for her life. Her wise grandfather gives her a third goal and tells her, "You must do something to make the world more beautiful."[6] I had always believed that it is our true nature to want to contribute to the well-being of others and make the world a better place.

As I searched for answers to my health, happiness and well-being, I realized that how a person feels — physically, mentally and emotionally — has a far-reaching effect upon their success and happiness. It frees up time to do other things besides managing illness and disease. It colors the perception of what people believe to be possible. I appreciated the fact that when people feel at their best, they are capable of being, doing and giving even more than they already do. They have greater energy and stamina to get things done. Their ability to focus and cope becomes effortless. Clarity and insight increase, and greater creativity becomes available for seeking solutions. It is easier to be optimistic, happy, flexible and confident. The ease and natural flow of life can then be fully experienced. This encourages the voice of heartfelt intuition and wisdom to be heard and makes life richer and more fun. Vitality and health create a natural willingness to make positive, meaningful changes and to follow through. Each person then has an even greater capacity to make the world more beautiful.

Miss Rumphius ignited a deep yearning in me to make my own meaningful contribution. I wanted to share my experiences and knowledge with those who were ready to improve the quality of their lives. By living life authentically, I hoped that I would inspire others to have the courage to live life on their own terms. I had so much that I wanted to experience and do. I knew that I had barely gotten started. As I rested against my pillows in a pool of sweat, I told myself that even though I was discouraged, I was not ready to give up on life yet.

My dad loves to tell a story about when I was five or six that illustrates my tenacity and spirit for never giving up. Our family and friends were enjoying a day of swimming at a lake in upstate New York. The kiddie section was roped off next to the adult swim area. My sister and I, being the youngest members of our group, were told we could only swim in the kiddie section. Well, that was not okay with me. I wanted to swim in the adult area, but the lifeguard said I was too little. I told both him and my dad that I was *not* too little.

The guard explained that I would have to pass a swim test by swimming the length of the adult area. Dad thought I could not do it, but I said I could, so he let me try. Much to everyone's amazement, I did manage to swim the full length of the adult section. I remember jumping in and not thinking about the distance I had to swim. I just did it. The experience was exhilarating with each stroke I took. This defining moment taught me to believe in myself, to never give up and to always persevere in what was true for me. If I had the desire, I would find a way to accomplish what I chose.

Chapter 7

We live too short and die too long.

Walter M. Bortz II

I lay in bed and tossed and turned as I struggled to take a breath. My pink cotton nightgown with white lace trim was soaked with urine and sweat. My bed, positioned against the wall, enabled me to see out the window onto the desert landscape of my backyard. Nothing of significance grew out there but low-lying prickly pear and scrub brushes. Tumbleweeds blew haphazardly around the rocky, barren landscape that stretched out over the acre of land. In the evening, I would watch the baby-blue sky blaze with reddish-orange clouds that never brought rain. The heat would slowly recede, and a cool, gentle breeze would playfully move the curtain around my window frame.

Over the next few days I would look out the window, but the landscape seemed to disappear. My mind became blank. I began to withdraw from the world around me. I did not recognize anyone who came to see me, and at times I did not even recognize my own children. I refused food, and just drank little sips of water when it was offered to me. Sometimes I did not even know where I was — and I did not care. Nothing at this point bothered me; my world fell strangely silent. I felt peaceful and almost happy for the first time since arriving in Arizona.

The days and nights became a blur. Then, one night, I quietly slipped out of my body. I turned and looked at the crumpled lump that lay on the bed, illuminated by the moonlight, with the realization that it belonged to me. I do not think I had much of a reaction to what I saw. I turned away, feeling a quiet wave of joy and adventure suddenly wash over me. I found myself moving through a passageway filled with light. There I was, surrounded by a peaceful, loving and welcoming group of "glowing balls of light." No words were exchanged, but instead, heartfelt feelings that created thoughts and ideas.

I remember bits and pieces about the experience. I have the impression that I was told many things. I thought, "How am I going to remember all of this?" I was immediately put at ease and "told" not to worry. When I needed the information it would be there for me, and I would think that it was my own thought. So now, when I have knowledge of something I could not possibly know, or a great idea that comes to me seemingly out of nowhere, I smile and nod and remember my experience. I am reminded that there is a great deal of support and unconditional love that is always present. I am never alone or forgotten.

I knew that sometimes, oftentimes, life did not work out the way I had hoped and dreamed it would. But I will never give up on my dreams — it is the stuff that life is made of. I now understood that health is first and foremost a state of mind. My body responded directly to my thoughts, which were supercharged by my emotions. In order to live a more fulfilling and meaningful life, I needed to stop reacting and start responding from the broader perspective of the unconditional love that I experienced on the other side. I needed to embrace this perspective, and focus on and appreciate the people, places and things that made me feel happy and good about myself. To be authentic meant saying and doing things that honored and reflected who I really am, who we all are: unconditional love. I learned through my adventure that we are here to grow, and to experience life for the joy and magic in it.

As quickly as I was gone from my bedroom, I was back in my body with a jolt, trembling and coughing up bloodstained mucus. The pain quickly returned. My throat felt as if it were on fire, and my rough skin felt hot, clammy and uncomfortable. I was too weak to cry out, but for a moment I had a powerful feeling of clarity and calm sweep through my body. I felt an overwhelming sense of relief, and then a warm, comforting, playful, softly swirling sensation moved through me that I could only describe as unconditional love. The moonlight was replaced by sunlight streaming into my bedroom. I could see particles of dust dancing in the cascading light. I knew beyond a shadow of a doubt that everything would eventually be fine.

That morning I dreamt that I jumped off a wooden dock into the cool, still waters of the lake in upstate New York where I swam as a child. I watched the blue-green water ripple out in all directions. To my right, I saw my father and a gaunt woman in a pink lace nightgown standing there on the dock, urging me forward. Surprised, I realized the woman was me! Smiling, I took a deep breath and cleared my mind. Determined, I put my head down into the water and blew bubbles. Then, doing a modified dog paddle, I made my way slowly and deliberately towards the far side of the dock.

Later that day, the doctor gave me some new medication and a treatment to open up my lungs so that I could breathe more easily. I felt no better, but I had become hopeful that my near-death experience would create monumental changes in my life. I wanted my health and my circumstances to somehow magically improve, with no effort on my part. I waited, but nothing seemed different to me. I was where I was. I had more insight, but nothing else. I was really disappointed. I felt frail and weak. My immune system was still so stressed and overburdened that it would take two years for me to climb out of that deep hole and start feeling somewhat normal. Even then, my health would still be challenged.

Due to my lack of energy, I decided to reorganize my life and priorities. I let go of the majority of my long-distance consulting business. I focused on my daughters, and took care of myself as best I could. My days were filled with driving the girls to their school and activities in Sedona. The public library became my second home. For two years, I lived in that small desert town on the outskirts of Sedona.

My next-door neighbors, an older couple who were interested in natural health and healing, became a lifeline for the girls and me. Life got back to some level of normalcy: I cooked, cleaned, shopped and took care of my daughters. We had play dates with their classmates and participated in school events, and I got to know some of the other moms. We hosted their class celebrations such as the Maypole festival and had evening programs around our large fire pit. The girls and I had our daily rituals that often included story time, games, baking and art projects. My exhaustion made it difficult to engage in the moment; I went through the motions of living. I felt frail, afraid and defeated. I continued to get sick.

My friends and family were losing patience. My mom would call and get frustrated with me. Three questions I got over and over again were: "What is it this time?" "Do you think it is probably all in your head?" and "If you have such a healthy diet and are doing all this natural stuff, then why are you so sick all the time?" I had no answers. I needed empathy and support, not sarcastic, judgmental one-liners. Was I doing something wrong? Was I failing my body and myself in some way?

My struggles, and the daily annoyances caused by my poor health, forced me to ask many questions I otherwise would probably have never considered. The questions I most thought about were: what is health, and what does it mean to be healthy? The word health comes from the Old English word "haelth" meaning wholeness or being whole.[7] Health is a complex concept at best, and there are many different modern definitions. The World Health Organization defines health as "a state of complete physical, mental and social well-being and not merely the absence of disease and infirmity."[8]

In his book *The Normal and the Pathological* (1943), Dr. George Canguilheim defined health as the body's ability to adapt to one's environment. He rejected the idea of normal or abnormal states of health. Health can be defined uniquely, based on each person's circumstances and their specific needs.[9] His insight made the individual the ultimate authority of his or her own health. I knew from my consulting business that what constitutes health varies based on perceptions, beliefs and circumstances. Health is defined by an individual's needs at a specific moment in time.

Health for me came down to a few simple questions: "What nutrients does my body need in greater or lesser quantity in order to work most effectively and efficiently?" For every reaction and function, my body requires minerals, vitamins, enzymes, proteins, healthy fats and carbohydrates as fuel in order to complete the tasks needed to keep me mentally, emotionally and physically fit. My next question was: "Is there anything that I am doing, or that is in my body, which is keeping it from properly performing its vital functions?" After my first dental surgery, I added a question, "Is my body being distracted, having to do things that take energy and resources that are otherwise needed for optimal daily functioning?"

Chapter 8

Life is one big transition.

Willie Stargell

As I slowly started to feel better, I took an inventory of my lifestyle and decided to make more changes. I joined a health club where I could take exercise classes and swim. I tried different diets and fine-tuned my eating habits. I meditated and used the guided relaxation CD *The Art of Letting Go* that I had produced back in Washington, D.C. I became even more interested in trying health and healing therapies. My next-door neighbor recommended a naturopathic doctor, who would become a key player in my quest for health. I spoke with many people and read a lot of books on various healing modalities.

I met many gifted practitioners and decided to work with a variety of therapies over time, which included different forms of massage, Rolfing, acupressure, acupuncture, meditation, visualization, chiropractic care, myopractic care and colon hydrotherapy. I cleansed the inside of my body and nourished it with vitamins and minerals, herbs and nutrient-rich foods. To increase my knowledge, I studied more about nutrition and received additional certifications for my efforts. I continued with the many stress-management techniques I had learned back in Washington, D.C., and I created many of my own as well.

I felt incredibly stuck. I began to question everything in my life. I struggled in yet another transitional zone, which felt uncomfortable and made me uneasy. I was unsure about how to get on with my life. I longed for real change. Then one afternoon, after I dropped the girls off at a birthday party in Sedona, I decided to take a drive. The unfamiliar neighborhood was nestled into a canyon with majestic red rocks. I hesitated as I passed a dead-end sign at the mouth of a street. My car stopped in the middle of the road. I backed up and took the left-hand turn, and found myself on a road that led straight into the National Forest. A "For Sale" sign sat on a half-acre of land, with a stucco house in the center of the property. Around the house were green grass, mature trees and a water feature that cascaded down a hill towards the front porch. If that was not perfect enough, the property had a spectacular view of the red rocks. I gasped as I excitedly reached for my cell phone and called my friend, a realtor. After I calmed down, she told me that the house was due to be sold in a few days. Needless to say, I was very disappointed and somewhat confused, because I felt such a strong connection with the property. I knew that it was mine, even though that did not make sense.

A few days later, I stood in the living room of my soon-to-be new home, admired the view and looked out at the orchard and gardens. The buyers had backed out at the last minute, deciding that the house was not a good fit for them. For me it was a fresh start. After two years of living in the desert, the girls and I moved to Sedona proper. Their father came to help us relocate. We loved our neighbors and our new home. Initially, the change improved my health considerably. Everything was going wonderfully, but after a few weeks of being in the house, the appliances, the fixtures and the heating and cooling system stopped working properly and started to fall apart. I could not help but notice the parallel between my body and the property I had just purchased. It seemed rather ironic.

Overwhelmed, I stood at the kitchen sink, looked out the window at the magnificent view and wondered what I had done. My other house had not sold yet. I closed my eyes and asked for a sign that would let me know I had made the right decision, that everything would be okay. Slowly I turned my gaze towards the empty lot in front of me. A steep hill ran down into the property. That is not what caught my eye, though. On the far side of the lot there was a pink-stucco wall with columns crowned with caps. I studied the wall and ran my eyes over its surface; it looked vaguely familiar to me.

As I stood there, an earlier image of a watercolor I had painted as a young teen surfaced in my mind. Back then, I had a recurring dream of looking out a kitchen window with a view of a steep, rolling yard, with scrub trees and a pink stucco wall divided by columns crowned with caps that bordered the far side of the property. I was stunned for a moment, as time stood still at my window. The memory of the watercolor and the dream came flooding back. This was the view I had painted! This was the view in my dreams! I took it as a positive sign that I was indeed in the right place. As I sighed with relief, I felt the weight of doubt and fear leave my shoulders.

After dealing with all the house crises, I turned my attention back to my career. I decided to work on a PhD in Natural Health with a school that offered long-distance learning. I wanted to learn more, both to help myself and to revitalize my career. I wanted to share what I had learned, by writing and lecturing. I felt that the PhD would give me the credentials to make my endeavors a success. My passion is to learn new things and share what I have learned. I began to search for answers to my questions about what constituted good health and well-being. Even though I liked the idea of earning a PhD, my exhaustion and brain fog caused me to struggle through the coursework. I refused to acknowledge that my heart was just not fully engaged.

I found myself interested in certain topics, which caused me to go off on tangents. I researched and studied those things that caught my attention. My memory also plagued me, as it had in college and graduate school. I found it slow going to study for exams. Being able to focus and retain information was difficult.

When I started working on my dissertation topic, *Stress and the Adrenal Glands: the search for life satisfaction, happiness and optimism*, I could not find the motivation to focus. I had to admit that I tried to force things to happen. I did not have the energy to complete anything, or to start new projects of any kind. I became more frustrated and concerned about my inability to follow through on my ideas.

Desperately, I tried to move out of the transitional zone where my life seemed to be permanently stuck. I wanted to feel passionate and fulfilled by my life. I thought the PhD would be the answer, but it did not work; nothing worked. Yes, my life obviously changed with the move into town. I was closer to everything now. I had made a few good friends. The girls attended a new school and were involved in different after-school activities.

I realized, however, that transition and change are two very different things. Change is often just that — change. It cannot take the place of the wisdom-induced expansiveness of that "no man's land" in which I found myself living. I did not understand the power of transition, the creative brilliance of that space. Instead I focused on the discomfort I felt. I had tried unsuccessfully to use change to rush through my transitional period that was now going into its third year.

Transition forced me to go deep within myself, into a type of metamorphosis that could not be rushed. Endings were happening all around me — I had left my beloved D.C., friends were dropping away and my business was shrinking. I found myself literally in the desert without a map to guide me. I felt alone, but was comforted by the girls as I focused on their school activities. I tried to keep myself busy. I made new friends when I decided to sit on the school's board. I chaired the Parent Partnership Committee that organized the volunteers for the classrooms and school fundraiser events. It was fun to meet new people and to be involved in so many different school activities. I also looked forward to their father's monthly visits as a way to stay connected to a feeling of normalcy.

My memory problems and exhaustion caused me to struggle with my coursework. To better understand how chronic fatigue syndrome (CFS) affected my body, I decided to study stress and the adrenals. The two adrenal glands are the size of walnuts. Each sits on top of a kidney. The adrenals perform many important functions. As part of the endocrine system, they produce adrenal hormones such as cortisol and adrenaline during the stress response. I think of the adrenals as being the body's "batteries" that supply energy and stamina. (Fig. 3)

Chronic stress brought on by an unhealthy lifestyle and/or diet, physical and/or emotional trauma, or repeated infections like pneumonia and high levels of toxicity in the body can result in unwanted illness.[10] I knew that the low hormonal output of my adrenal glands (sometimes referred to as adrenal fatigue) was happening for a reason. The adrenals were a piece of a larger puzzle. I realized that illness and disease just does not affect one part of the body; the whole body is interconnected and must make adjustments.

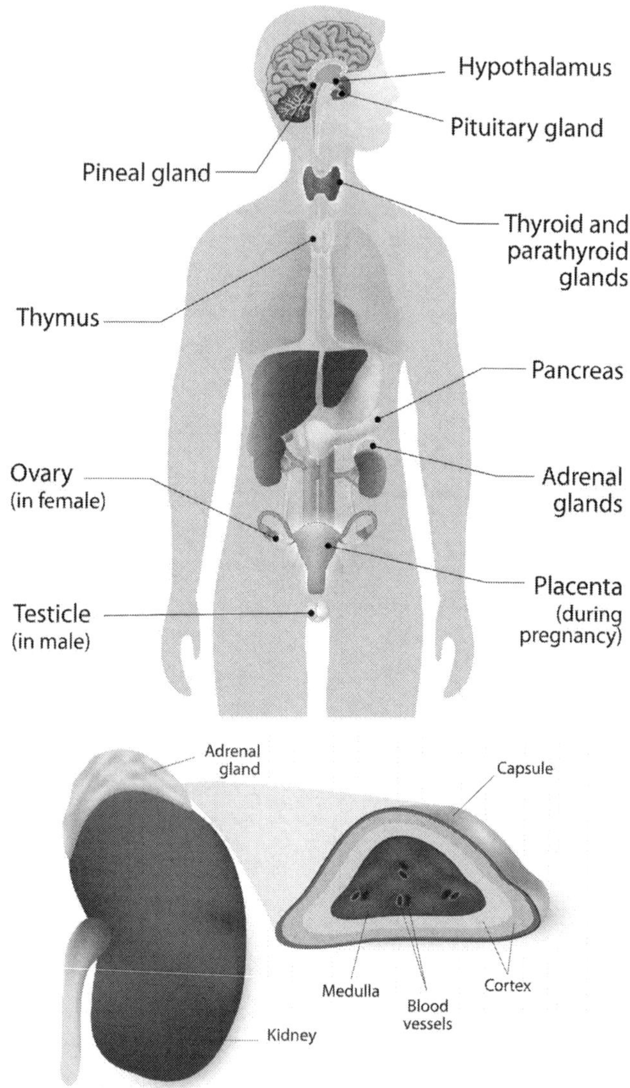

Figure 3. The endocrine system and adrenal glands.

To compensate for the reduced adrenal hormone output, unhealthy changes occur in the body's metabolism of fat, carbohydrate and protein. Blood pressure and blood sugar problems can occur.[11] The adrenal glands produce the hormone aldosterone. Too little or too much aldosterone can unbalance the body's fluid and electrolytes. This results in chronic dehydration and creates imbalances in the brain, heart and cardiovascular system.[12]

It seemed to me that my adrenal glands contributed to my CFS symptoms. I reasoned that if I could just figure out the stressor that kept my body in this constant state of vigilance and prolonged stress, I could remove it so that my body could heal.

I learned everything I could on the subject of adrenal fatigue. I spoke with experts and practitioners alike. Yet I could not figure out exactly what the stressor might be. Every time I tried to build my adrenals up with nutrients, and follow my healthy lifestyle, it did not work. I did everything I knew to do: reduce stress, make lifestyle changes, get plenty of rest, hydrate myself with clean, fresh water, and practice gentle exercise. I addressed my adrenals' nutritional needs, I worked on my own personal growth, and I continued to create my own stress-management techniques. Why did I get only partially satisfactory results? What information was I missing?

In the meantime, I had developed other problems since my bout with pneumonia. For example, I would be in the middle of a sentence and my voice would just trail off and stop. It would drive my daughters crazy. They would look at me and say "Mom, where are you? You did not finish what you were saying." It was weird because I had some awareness of this, but I lacked the energy to keep talking, and at some point, no more words would come out. During conversations I had trouble finding words, and I needed to pause and search for them. My mind would get so tired for no apparent reason. It was maddening and embarrassing.

I become so focused on what was wrong in my life that everything that was wrong grew and got bigger. It took more of my focus and daily energy to deal with my health. I had unknowingly put myself into a place of deep unhappiness, and I could see no way out. I thought that things would get better if I kept myself busy. The PhD was my attempt to distract myself, but my mind did not buy it. Schoolwork became something else I had to do, another stressor. Studying and learning became a chore.

I yearned to have my creativity back, and to be able to sit down and write again. I wanted to share my wisdom and experiences with others. I wanted to put together programs that would change people's lives in meaningful, useful and profound ways. I wanted to offer highly valuable and quality-oriented books, products and programs. I had accomplished this with the success of my consulting business back in Washington, D.C., and I wanted more.

I knew that first I had to get through this stagnant period. I had to regain the health that I had mysteriously lost. One day, I would share my experiences in an authentic manner with people who could benefit and feel inspired not to give up on themselves, their health or their lives. I knew the time was growing closer to that happy day, but I had no idea of how to get there. I likened my life to an old car with a dead battery and an engine that would not turn over. As time passed, I did my best to accept where I was in my life. I focused on the beauty, and all the good things, like my daughters. I got through each day as best I could, did whatever it took, and worked to maintain my health. The key was to find relief and soothe myself by remembering that I was doing the best I possibly could.

Then, without warning, I came down with pneumonia again. My girls took over running the house. Friends helped out by driving the girls to school and to the grocery store. I felt heartbroken at my inability to champion my health. I desperately wanted to regain my energy and vitality. I had always been successful with whatever I put my mind to, with the exception of improving my health. I felt pretty discouraged as my body slowly recovered from the pneumonia.

I was in a vicious cycle: I would wake up sick and tired. This made me frustrated and annoyed. My mind would try to figure out why I was sick and tired, but there were no real answers. So my mind would start to make up reasons, listing symptoms and things that had happened that week that were stressful. That did nothing but put me in a bad mood. To work myself out of that mood, I would take some action to distract myself, usually some kind of project, which would end up unsuccessful and unsatisfying. Then, I would have something else to point to and say, "Things just are not working out for me." This time I decided to take on the project of my website. I hired a consultant to help me with the design and the technical aspects. I spent a great deal of money. The end product was very disappointing, because I was not clear about what I really wanted to say or do. I was just spinning my wheels.

Chapter 9

When we are no longer able to change a situation — we are challenged to change ourselves.

Victor E. Frankl

My girls were growing up. Soon, I would become an "empty-nester" when they left for college. That thought somewhat terrified me. Most of my identity was tied to being a single mother. My social life revolved around the girls' school and activities. I decided to join a women's circle in an effort to make new friends, independent of my daughters. It was a fun group of women, all different ages, both married and single. Some worked; others were retired. One evening, we sat in a circle and each one of us spoke about the four things that we most wanted in our lives. When it was my turn I said that the four things I chose were peace of mind, health, service to others and love. I shifted my weight in my chair and felt something stir deep inside me. I cleared my throat as words poured out of me. I said that I was lonely and I felt ready to date. I told them that I longed for male companionship, and a loving relationship in which we both could grow. What I wished for was someone I could really talk to, someone who could take long walks and hikes with me. Someone I could snuggle. Many of the women nodded their heads sympathetically as my cheeks became red hot with embarrassment.

I took a deep breath and felt something release deep inside my heart. I had not planned on saying any of this — I did not know I felt that way. I was astonished! What I said next surprised me. Actually, it shocked me. I told them that I was ready to marry again, that I wanted to share my life with someone and have someone share his life with me. I sat back in my chair in disbelief at what I had just heard. I tried to fathom what had just happened while the group silently acknowledged my heartfelt outpouring.

My wish was not specific enough: Two weeks later, a loving companion with four paws and a tail became a part of my family. I am certainly not complaining, because Mr. Wiggles is the best. A three-month old rescue dog became my constant companion and confidant. "The Wiggs," a white Bichon Frise, enjoys long walks and hikes, and loves to snuggle. Be careful what you wish for!

The girls' Pilates instructor knew that my younger daughter wanted a dog in the worst way. Her neighbor was searching for the perfect home for a cute little puppy rescued from a puppy mill. Several times that week, I received calls about the dog. I barely had the energy to take care of myself and my business, the girls and our home, let alone a puppy. I ignored her pleas until I decided to find someone to take the dog. A family I knew agreed to meet the little guy. I called the woman who was temporarily caring for the puppy. We had a nice conversation. When she told me that she was juicing carrots to help repair the dog's digestive tract, and had him on an herbal remedy, my ears perked up. I told her the girls and I would be right over to get the puppy. We would take him sight unseen. I knew in my heart that he was ours. Resistance was futile.

The following year, I met the man who would become my husband. My world quickly changed the evening he told me of his plans to include me in his life, after only a few weeks of dating. Earlier that afternoon, I'd received an email from the school where I was working on my PhD in Natural Health. With one click of the mouse, I learned that the school had closed. As I stared at the computer screen, I froze in my chair. My PhD, which I had spent the past five years working on, along with the tuition I had paid and the dreams for my future, were gone in the blink of an eye.

I had been hopeful that the PhD would help redefine my career. I'd felt it would give me a new purpose when my girls left for college. My eyes brimmed with warm, salty tears. I consoled myself with the thought that I did not need the initials after my name for me to be the authority of my own life. Life would unfold in its own way, and would show me the direction to find purpose, meaning, fulfillment, love and health. I just needed to let go and trust.

As I sat there in shock and disbelief, another email popped in; this one was from the man I was dating. I took a deep breath to gather myself. I did not expect what I was about to read. He wanted to let me know how he felt about me and how much he enjoyed our time together. He also mentioned that he planned to ask me to marry him. I pushed my chair away from the table that held my computer, the tips of my chair legs making a slight screeching noise against the wooden floorboards. I shook as my heart pounded in my ears. Something shifted abruptly in me as I struggled to regain my balance. Within a few minutes, the direction of my life had totally changed course.

After a whirlwind romance, we were engaged.

My happiness soon faded, however, into concern and more stress. I endured a succession of respiratory illnesses and flus that left me feeling more drained. After I recovered, the lymph glands in my neck, especially on the right side, became much more swollen and slightly more sore than they had been in the past. I was doing everything I could to keep my body as healthy as possible. Over the years I had tried every healthy diet and all kinds of alternative health treatments. I had worked with a naturopathic doctor, and I was taking a few select vitamins, minerals and herbs to support my immune system, adrenals and overall health. I drank spring water. I juiced fruits and vegetables. I was in bed early every night, slept eight hours or more, and napped. I walked every day with Wiggles and exercised a few times a week, either stretching, doing Pilates or yoga, walking or taking short hikes. I meditated and listened to my relaxation CDs.

On really bad days, I sometimes had a fleeting thought in the back of my mind that maybe I had done something wrong. How could I be so healthy up until my twenties, and then seemingly out of nowhere become so sick? It did not make sense. Things did not add up here. I believed that wellness and health are a natural state of being. I knew that given the proper environment, the body would heal itself, and that energy, stamina, clarity and balance could and would be restored.

I felt that I had given my body the best environment that I possibly could in which to heal. For goodness' sake, I even traded the stressful hustle and bustle of the East Coast for a more quiet and peaceful existence among the red rocks of Sedona. I made many changes in my life, but stubbornly my symptoms would not go away. My body continued to speak to me in a language I did not understand.

I did cleanses and lymphatic massages for my swollen lymph nodes. During the massages, my lymph would let go for a moment and then immediately fill back up. My lymph nodes continued to be lumpy. Well-meaning people questioned me: If I knew so much and was doing all this work, then why was my lymph still swollen? Why was it acting this way? The tone of their voice was, "See, this natural stuff does not work; you are wasting your time and money." Deep down, I knew that was not the case. If I was not doing all of those things, I would not be able to function as well as I was. Still, I had no answers for them. I felt that my lymph was doing its job by holding some kind of waste material. But what was it holding? It would be almost two more years until I would discover the answer.

Chapter 10

The body is a sacred garment.

Martha Graham

It was a cool and cloudy morning as I stood next to my doctor in front of a small video screen that hung on a bland-colored tan wall. The results had come back from the MRI on my neck. Restlessly I shifted my weight from one foot to the other; I realized I had been holding my breath. I was hopeful that the MRI would not show anything of significance. Or would it?

My general practitioner had requested that I see a specialist because the lymph nodes on the right side of my neck had become more swollen and sore than usual. I told this specialist that since my early twenties, the lymph nodes in my neck, particularly on the right side, had been swollen — a little at first and then more over the years. I referred to that area of my neck as "a bag of frozen peas." Those small, hard little lumps were lymph nodes that sometimes became slightly sore. Lymph is a clear, watery fluid found throughout the body that delivers nutrients and oxygen to the cells while collecting waste for disposal. An important part of the immune system, lymph is more plentiful than blood. Lymph nodes act as filters for harmful substances and contain immune cells that help fight infection. (Fig. 4)

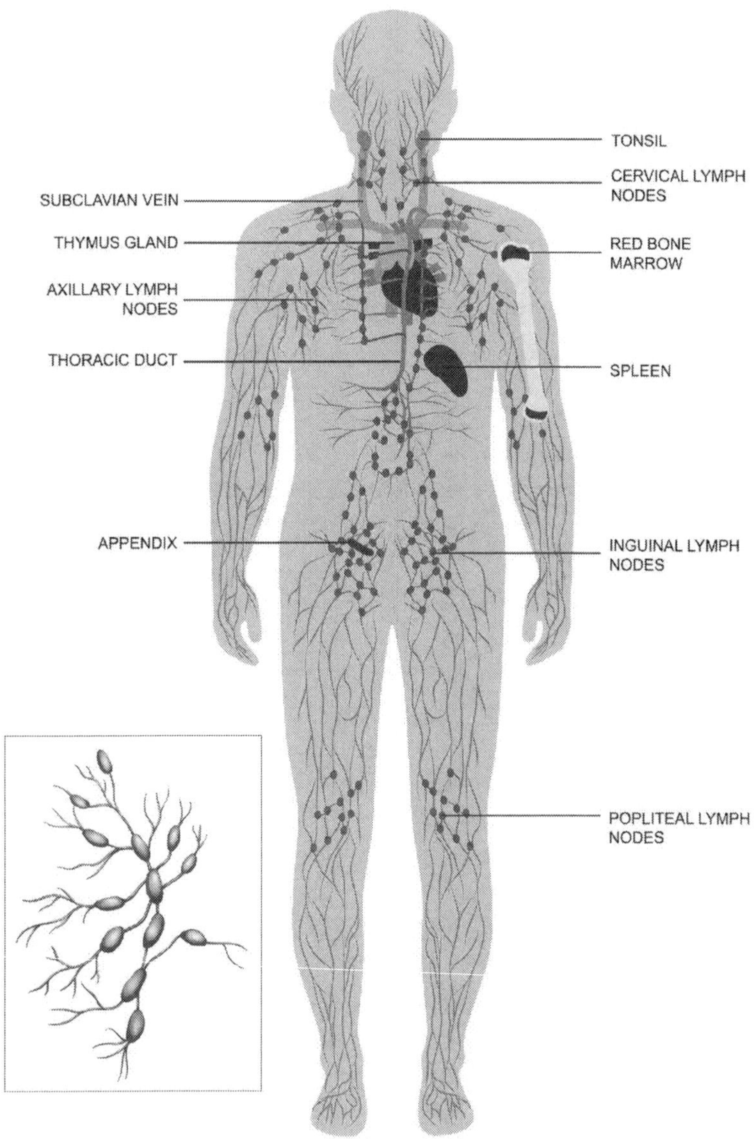

Fig. 4 Lymph system and lymph

I was more perplexed than worried about the state of my lymph. I reasoned that there was no way that I could be seriously ill. Monitoring my health had become a continuous project since my early twenties, when I began to experience all kinds of symptoms seemingly out of the blue. As I stood there in the doctor's office, I told the doctor that I was doing everything I could to keep my body as healthy as possible. I thought about all the healthy diets and the many alternative health treatments I had done in order to give my body a more suitable environment in which to heal. I was somewhat able to manage my energy level, stamina and well-being, but I'd never fully gained back my vibrant good health. I grimaced and shook my head.

The doctor turned on the screen to display the MRI image. I closed my eyes for a moment, feeling soothed by the darkness, as I gathered the courage to look at the screen. I slowly opened one eye and then the other. The images from the MRI showed that the lymph nodes in my neck and clavicle area were indeed very swollen. That was nothing new. But the quantity of the swollen lymph was very disturbing. The doctor looked concerned. Breaking the silence, he quietly told me that our next step would be to biopsy the lymph. We needed to see what we were dealing with, and to rule out the diagnosis of lymphoma — and we needed to do it soon. He said he was very sorry and wished he had better news for me.

My mind raced. As I stood there, the room began to sway. I planted my feet firmly on the ground. My cheeks became hot and flushed. A wave of anger crashed down over me and moved quickly throughout my body. I took a deep breath to try to calm myself. My voice shook as I told him that under no circumstances was anyone going to biopsy any of my lymph. If there was cancer, and we cut into the lymph, we risked spreading it through its vast network in my body. My fiancé quickly spoke up and said that the lymph nodes in my neck were doing their job and protecting the rest of my body. He sounded hopeful. Protecting it? Yes, I thought, but from what?

I wondered aloud: If that was what the lymph nodes looked like in my neck, how must they look in the rest of my body? My shoulders shook as hot tears ran quickly down my cheeks, momentarily obstructing my vision. All of a sudden, my thoughts turned back in time to my college dorm room, with the poster of the box by Joseph Cornell. I had a fleeting thought of Bia, the Medici princess, and how cruel it was that her little red ball was out of her reach. My mind shifted gears as the phrase, "You will think it is your own thought," appeared in my mind from my near-death experience. My heartbeat sped up and pounded away in my temples. I knew I was in danger of letting my mind run away with me.

I took a moment to reach inside myself and watch the anger as it continued to swirl through my body. I noticed my shoulders suddenly relax. Anger created a boundary, and protected me from the helplessness and hopelessness that would have made me feel like a victim. I had handled my health for the past thirty years, and even though I felt momentarily defeated, I was not about to give up. No, I would not step out of my power and no, I would not have a biopsy done. Instinctively, I knew beyond a shadow of doubt that a biopsy, in this case, would not lead to anything productive. I would stand my ground and find other options. I would handle this in my own way. Again.

Chapter 11

There is one consolation in being sick; and that is the possibility that you may recover to a better state than you were ever in before.

Henry David Thoreau

When I returned from viewing the MRI, my doctor called and said that he had spoken to the specialist. Based on the MRI, he would like to run some tests and look into other possibilities. He was well aware of my healthy lifestyle and my preference for natural health, and he felt it was worthwhile to look into other alternatives. Based on all the blood tests we did, my doctor decided that I had the Epstein-Barr virus. That would explain my exhaustion, and perhaps why the lymph nodes in my neck might be swollen.

Epstein-Barr virus (EBV), he explained to me, is a type of herpes virus that causes infectious mononucleosis and can also be associated with different cancers. EBV attacks the cells that line the mouth and throat. It can affect the lungs, liver, bone marrow and eyes, and it is often confused with chronic fatigue syndrome. To me, this sounded like a better prognosis than lymphoma. The doctor explained that there was no treatment for the virus, and that I should continue my healthy lifestyle. He cautioned me that I would need to watch the swollen lymph nodes and have them checked regularly. I promised that I would.

In the past, when I put my mind to something I had always been able to accomplish it, with the exception of improving my health. I was tired of the labels that everyone placed on me, such as chronic fatigue, with a host of other infections running amuck inside of me — and now the Epstein- Barr virus. No offense to Doctors Epstein and Barr, but I had lost patience with my body and myself. I refused to identify myself as an illness. I thought of myself as a human being and a woman, with a conversation going on in my body that I could not translate. I just could not figure out what was making me so sick. I was doing everything I could to improve my body's inner environment. I hated the exhaustion, the foggy thinking, the general malaise and the weird symptoms that would pop up out of nowhere. The mental and emotional stress that this caused was almost worse than the symptoms themselves. The best I could do was to maintain a low standard of wellness. I longed to bring back the vitality I had experienced as a teen. What I disliked most of all was when people tried to comfort me by saying that this was all just a natural part of the aging process — even when I was in my late twenties. If I had a dollar for every time someone said that to me I would be a very wealthy (albeit unhealthy) woman.

Chapter 12

Bad times have a scientific value. These are occasions a good learner would not miss.

Ralph Waldo Emerson

As if my life were not full of enough drama at this point, my husband decided to accept a job — in Houston, where he'd grown up — right after our wedding. Initially I saw this move as a chance to start a new life for us all. However, there were plenty of signs along the way that clearly pointed out that we were not welcome in Houston. Regardless, my husband was going anyway. I had a choice to make: go or stay. So many emotions swam through me that I felt confused, and longed for peace. Sitting in that void of indecision and nothingness was uncomfortable. Instead, I filled that space with lots of action to try and force a comfortable flow of decisiveness. It did not work. The stress of the situation, my search for a new place to live, putting my house on the market and the move itself — these had all placed me back in survival mode.

My husband left for Houston shortly after our wedding, and I was left to fend for myself with my girls. I felt overwhelmed, unsupported and alone, even though so many wonderful people from Sedona came to help me pack, get organized and wipe away my tears. I began to experience aches and pains in my body that were unfamiliar to me. I found that I had less and less energy to accomplish all the things I needed to do; the energy seemed to just drain out of me. My body screamed No! But I was too afraid and stubborn to listen.

When I arrived in Houston, nothing worked out. Our rental was not ready. Our neighbor did not like the moving van out front and called the police. Registering the girls to attend their new school was a nightmare. The simplest things became a monumental struggle, like attempting to change my car registration and license, which took over four visits to the Department of Motor Vehicles. To make matters worse, I constantly got lost in the city of Houston, even with a GPS! Poor Mr. Wiggles did not fare very well either, having gotten his first case of fleas.

My health continued to deteriorate. I spent a lot of time sleeping, but I woke up feeling as tired and sad as I did before my nap. Doing anything took great effort. I began to have intense night sweats, and aches and pains in my neck, shoulders and legs. I went to a chiropractor and a massage therapist, and I did physical therapy, but I could get no relief. I experienced a high level of anxiety that I had never known. I longed for my quiet life back in Sedona. My body was on high alert, telling me again that everything was wrong.

My mouth also responded in kind. In a matter of days I began to collect thick deposits of tartar on the inside of my bottom front teeth that no amount of brushing or flossing could remove or keep from forming. I had several professional teeth cleanings, but the buildup would always come back within a few days. The dentist I visited had no suggestions, but he *was* concerned that so much tartar was forming at such an alarming rate.[13]

Friends and acquaintances from Sedona stayed in touch with me on a regular basis. I received phone calls and cards, as well as emails of encouragement and support, on a daily basis. I tried hard to give Houston a chance and make it work, but I was failing miserably. My older daughter had the common sense to go back home to Sedona after a week of overcrowded classrooms. She knew that this was the wrong place for her. My husband was not available, having his own issues to deal with, and he made no time for our relationship. I was sad and angry all at once. I felt betrayed. I wanted to create a relationship based on communication, connection, honesty and friendship — and I thought that was what he had wanted as well. I became plagued by the question of whether I should stay in Houston, or throw in the towel and go back home to Sedona.

One afternoon when I went to the bank to straighten out yet another problem, the woman from across the desk looked at me intently after listening to why I was there. Then, out of the blue, she changed the subject and asked me why I was in Houston. Startled by her question, I told her it was because my daughters and I needed a change. My new husband wanted to return to his hometown. Actually, my older daughter had assessed the situation in Houston and had the sense to return to Sedona. The bank officer shook her head and said, "No, no. This will not do! You need to get yourself and your other daughter on a plane and go back home to Sedona!" I was surprised by what she had just said; where had that come from? As I composed myself, I told her that I was not a quitter, and that I needed to give Houston more time. Shaking her head, she repeated what she had said.

Somehow, questions asked in earnest are always answered. The following week I received four signs that made the decision to return home easy. After school, I took my daughter to get her hair cut. I sat in the salon waiting area and had brought my mail with me for something to read. I opened a letter from the insurance company that insured my home in Sedona. The letter informed me that my homeowners insurance was being cancelled since I was no longer living there (even though I had friends staying in the house). Before I had a chance to process this news, my cell phone rang. My real estate agent on the other end told me that the couple buying my house had just backed out with no explanation. He would try to get more information. Before I could even catch my breath, a text appeared from my husband. He had quit his job and was taking some time for himself. He would contact me in a few days. With no time to respond, I helplessly looked over at my daughter.

This was the last straw. Literally, her hair looked as if someone had put a small bowl on her head and closed their eyes. Strands of hair stood up on top of her head. The stylist had butchered my daughter's hair; it was the worst haircut I had ever seen. I laughed as tears of relief rolled down my cheeks. There was no doubt that our time in Houston, thankfully, was coming to an end.

The small townhouse I had rented summed up my six-week experience. The plumbing kept backing up. One morning as I was making breakfast, my daughter flushed the upstairs toilet. I heard a loud whooshing sound as wastewater from the toilet bowl above came raining down on me from the air-conditioning vent above my head. Yes, the air-conditioning vent! Life could not get any worse, I thought at the time, but it did. Houston did not want me and Sedona would not let me go.

My daughter, a few neighbors and Wiggles became my lifeline during those six weeks. They were my pillars of unconditional love and strength. I had to find my sense of humor, because everything that happened was so absurd. I felt so raw inside. I began to laugh until I cried. Everywhere, people and signs were telling me to go back home to Sedona. Yes — HOME to Sedona. New friends in Houston began to appear out of nowhere to support me in my decision. I met some wonderful people whom I will always cherish.

From my experiences in Houston, I had an "aha moment" one morning as I took the Wiggs out for his morning walk. I realized that my stress had been created by the belief that what was happening to me should not be happening. My mind intently focused on this fact. From my Houston experience, I observed how the mind loves to be in charge. My mind loved to ask questions that had no answers and were a waste of time to think about. Yes, things were not good, but I now understood that I had allowed myself to innocently be sucked into other people's drama. I had allowed myself to be sucked into the stories and endless questions that my mind generated — because truthfully, up until that moment, I really did not know any better.

I thought about a recurring dream. I was in a cavernous building — sometimes a grand home, sometimes a library. The buildings were very old and the proportions were on a grand scale, not on a human scale like a small, cozy room. The spaces were cold and dank, and felt less than inviting. The rooms were in disrepair. The faded walls that were once painted brilliant colors were marred by water damage. The once beautiful and new draperies that covered the windows were dirty, torn and tattered. I would sometimes be there with my first husband or other people, but the one constant in the dream would be the leaky ceilings. Water would flow down the walls. I would wake up from these dreams puzzled by their meaning.

Then, while walking the Wiggs during the last few days I was in Houston, the meaning occurred to me. The buildings symbolized my mind. The water pouring down the walls signified my loss of energy. The dream meant that I used my mind in ways that did not serve me. My thoughts, for the most part, were unproductive, and a further drain upon my energy. I worried about people and things over which I had no control. I tried to "make it better" for everyone. The fact of the matter was that I had to take care of me, and do what was best for me, and not factor other people into the equation. Two questions needed to be asked to help me get clear: "What is true for me in this very moment?" and "What is it that I need?" This was not being selfish, but in fact being selfless. I had nothing to offer anyone if I did not take care of me first, and nurture and nourish myself. This revelation held untold new possibilities.

From that day forward, when I walked the Wiggs, I began to play a game with myself. I pretended that my mind was a TV set that I could watch. I would pay attention to what my mind thought about, and I discovered something: my mind was terrorizing me. Maybe that is too strong a word, but my mind created worst-case scenarios of situations. These "movies" would play over and over again. I realized that they brought up deep feelings of dread and fear that were difficult to shake. They brought up feelings of anxiety, sadness and anger from deep inside. There were no solutions, no empathy and no relief. My mind's mindless chatter would berate me for what it considered mistakes that I had made. My mind would worry about things that really were none of my business. Unbeknownst to me, I let my mind run the show, and I bought into it — hook, line and sinker. Yes, the "movies" were loosely based on fact, but I allowed my mind to take what had happened and distort it because that is what the mind does when left to its own devices. As I continued to watch my mind on these walks with Wiggles, I was rather amazed.

I came to the conclusion that being aware of my thoughts, and consciously choosing what I thought about, was important. I needed to care about how I felt! I could not control other people or things that had happened, but I could decide if I would give them any power and let them ruin my life. It came down to being aware of how I felt, and focusing on things that made me feel better — no matter what went on around me. I needed a new perspective. I did not see things as "mistakes," as my mind was insisting. I knew in my heart that there were no mistakes, only experiences that resulted from decisions I had made. I realized I could make other choices. It was time to take charge and change the channel.

Chapter 13

There's no place like home!

Dorothy, The Wizard of Oz

I could not get back home to Sedona fast enough. Life had taken on a surreal quality, and I was ready to try and regain my footing. A feeling of dread clung to me that I could not seem to shake. I wanted to make a clean start, but my health continued to decline. I was even more prone to infections; I felt even greater exhaustion. I tried to stop my health from deteriorating further, but the things I had done in the past to keep myself going no longer worked. I was in trouble and I did not know what to do. I felt overwhelmed. My body was too depleted, stressed and tired to withstand any more cleanses. My digestion was so bad that the herbs, supplements and foods I ate did not get fully digested and assimilated by my body. I started to gain weight, although I continued with my healthy diet, and could barely choke down food. More symptoms appeared or worsened. My eyesight became strained, and I needed a stronger prescription in order to read. The night sweats I experienced in Houston became more intense; I would wake up soaked, with my lymph nodes and the area around my liver swollen and tender. My liver would ache and feel colicky. I felt discouraged and angry with myself.

The stress from my Houston experience opened a floodgate of new problems. I started having fevers on and off, and developed arthritis in my right hand. Now I could no longer garden, or comfortably hold a pencil, or wear my favorite gold ring shaped like two dolphins. One day when I went to my doctor, my blood pressure was dangerously low (60/40). I constantly struggled with dehydration no matter how much water I drank. I knew my adrenals were terribly stressed out and exhausted. I could not take much more. I was frustrated and scared. I started to have anxiety attacks. I knew something had to change — and I knew that something was me.

I stood in front of my bathroom mirror and really looked at myself. I saw a woman who was no longer young. She had dark circles under her eyes and swollen lymph nodes in her neck. I looked deep into my eyes and saw a woman who felt defeated, and cheated out of a healthy "happily ever after." I saw a woman who had started to second-guess herself and wonder if this was all there was to life. I cried and felt sorry for myself. Since returning from Houston, I had nightmares that would wake me up with my own screams. I began to experience mornings like I'd had during my divorce. I would open my eyes and find myself lying in a cold sweat on my bed. I felt dread and disappointment that I was waking up to another day where nothing had changed.

I tried to go back to my old life in Sedona and pretend that nothing had changed — but it had. I was no longer the same person I was before I went to Houston. It was time to let go of my old life, my beliefs, hopes and dreams. This time I had to admit defeat, to admit failure. But it was all right somehow. I understood that sometimes the only response I could make to life was to let go and move into the void of transition that I had tried so hard to steer clear of for all these years. I would survive the emptiness and aloneness. I would survive the feelings that I had abandoned myself, and been betrayed by others.

I realized that I could no longer make a fresh start by the act of sheer will, the way I had done in the past. I was much too sick and tired for that now. Putting together plans and trying to take action was a waste of time. To make changes is one thing, but to transition out of one life and into another takes patience, courage and hope. It was time to go inward and just let go of who I thought I was, and what I thought I wanted. Perseverance was not appropriate here. I needed to sit still and be silent, in order to see what would happen next.

One afternoon I received an email from a realtor about my house, which had been off the market for about a month. She explained that she had seen my house, and that a couple was very much interested in purchasing it, if I was still interested in selling. To say the least, I was surprised. I did not answer her email for a few days — not because I had to decide if I wanted to sell or not, but because I needed to figure out how I wanted to respond. This felt very important.

When I finally sat down to write, I thanked her for this opportunity to think about my plans and what was important to me. I told her that the past two years had been two of the most disappointing and traumatic of my life. From these unwanted experiences, I realized that for a long time I had undervalued what I had created in my life, and more importantly, I had undervalued myself. Now that I was aware of this fact, I would never allow it to happen again.

I thought about how unique my home is, and about all the remodeling I had done over the years. The new, beautiful hardwood flooring; the natural-stone tile in the bathrooms; the beautiful, multicolored Cooper Stone surround on my fireplace; the built-in book cases and cabinets I had designed; the decorative metal railing on my porch and the soft, feminine colors of the painted walls in the house — everything reflected who I am. I then thought about all the improvements I'd made on my property, including my fruit trees, which I had lovingly nursed back to health, as well as the herb and vegetable garden, and the wildflower and rose garden, that I'd planted.

I wrote in my email that my property and my home are a reflection of my hopes and dreams — and most importantly, a reflection of me. I then quoted a selling price that surely caused her to gasp. I finished the email by stating that I would be happy to live here until someone came along who appreciated and valued what I had built as much as I did.

This email proclaimed a shift in my perceptions about myself and about life. My home needed to become a sanctuary of unconditional love, free from self-criticism. I was ready to let go and allow life to unfold inside of me and around me, which felt liberating. I was willing to trust the process, knowing that if I stayed receptive and clear about what I wanted and needed, the right people, resources and opportunities would surely come my way. I saw life and personal growth as an endless process that has no beginning or end. They cycle through death, growth and rebirth just like the fourteen fruit trees in my orchard.

My orchard had a lot to teach me. The trees respond to life according to the seasons; I needed to honor that cycle inside myself. There would be a spring, with the budding of new growth, and then a summer where the new and improved me would blossom and bear fruit. Fall would be the harvest, and the celebration of me. Winter was the time to let go of who I thought I had become, in order to make room for the growth of yet a more authentic me. Life is a process — or better yet, a journey that has its own destination. I had rarely known my destination, even though I had set goals and intentions for myself. Houston had served as my Oz and I, like Dorothy, had returned home again, not only to Sedona — but also, more importantly, to myself.

There's no place like home.

Chapter 14

Synchronicity is choreographed by a great, pervasive intelligence that lies at the heart of nature, and is manifest in each of us through intuitive knowledge.

Deepak Chopra

When I returned from Houston, I took a part-time job to work with plants and herbs that were being made into herbal remedies. The company's relaxed environment and interesting employees made it fun to work there. Best of all, the organically grown and wild plants sustained and nurtured me with their life force and beauty.

I worked with a very unusual plant, the carnivorous pitcher plant. It is quite beautiful, with its long, light-green stem and alluring, delicate-looking pink-and-white leaves that have evolved into a goblet-shaped cup called a "pitfall trap." The pitcher plant produces nectar, which seduces unsuspecting insects. They land on the plant's slippery rim, fall into the pool of liquid and drown. The insect's body is slowly digested and dissolved by the stomach-acid-like secretions in the nectar. The digestive juices of the plant are sticky, with a strong, unpleasant odor of decay.

To prepare the pitcher plant, a knife cuts off the pitfall trap, and then slices the stem open vertically. Separating the sides of the cut stem reveals bugs in different stages of digestion. With a black, fine, almost soil-like consistency, the remains of the digested insects lie near the bottom of the stem.

No one liked to work with these plants because of their stickiness and odor. I did not mind. Handling these plants was actually very healing for me and gave me a sense of relief and purpose. The pitcher plant belongs to the genus Nepenthes. Ancient Greek poets mentioned a potion called Nepenthe that caused forgetfulness of sorrows and misfortune. I could definitely appreciate this, and I was hopeful that I could forget my own sorrows and misfortunes. I was so traumatized and heartbroken. I looked out through the years of my life, and realized that nothing had worked out remotely the way I had thought it would. My hopes and dreams seemed like fairy tales to which I had foolishly clung, now that hope seemed but a distant memory. Perhaps worst of all, I felt that I had let down my family and friends, and most of all, myself. I was grateful to be given the opportunity to work with these unique plants, which I hoped would help me find a new perspective on forgiveness.

One afternoon, something incredible happened. While I prepared the pitcher plants to be soaked and cleaned, I listened to my mind chatter away about how things were so terrible. I berated myself as I sliced open the stem of the plant in front of me. The stench was vile. I noticed the thick mass of digested bugs in different stages. As I moved further down the stem, the insect remains turned into a fine, black-colored, sand-like mass. There seemed to be nothing unusual about this plant.

I was not ready for what happened next. When I pulled back the sides of the lower half of the stem I had just carefully cut (expecting to find only the finely digested insect remains), a white moth flew out! The moth's wings were wet with digestive juices, but it managed to fly out of the pitcher plant's stem. It sat on my arm for the next half hour, drying off, before it flew out into the hallway.

I wish I could have captured the look on the faces of the other people in the room, as well as my own. My mind raced with questions, with possibilities. How was this moth able to survive such harsh circumstances, and seem none the worse for wear? A moth's wings have a thick layer of tiny scales, made from hairs, that makes them look slightly furry. Some moths are able to wrap their wings around their body when they rest. I gathered that this moth's wings had served as a form of protection from the digestive juices of the pitcher plant, enabling it to survive the hostile conditions.

Any of the employees there could have picked up this specific stem from the six large boxes of these plants, but I was the one who did. I was dumbfounded that a live moth had survived the harsh environment inside the pitcher plant. As the white moth perched on my arm, I smiled softly to myself. I was reminded of the importance of setting healthy, strong internal boundaries for myself. These boundaries are essential for protecting my integrity and self-respect.

The moth's wings protected the insect, and kept it alive, in the harsh environment of the pitcher plant. For me, the moth represented my hopes and dreams. The moth had survived its ordeal, and the message was clear that I would also. My hopes and dreams were far from dead; they were, in fact, what kept me going. I had faith that my health and my life would get better. I, too, was going to get out alive. Symbolically speaking, the moth has strong healing abilities and encourages the release of unwanted influences and experiences. This moth reminded me to be optimistic, to never stop looking for light in the dark passages of my life. Like the moth, I was about to take flight. I was headed for uncharted areas to explore a final option for my health.

Chapter 15

We must be willing to let go of the life we've planned, so as to have the life that is waiting for us.

Joseph Campbell

A few weeks later, I took my daughter for her orthodontic checkup. Usually she is seen right away, but today we waited in the spacious, colorful and cheerful waiting room. There were comfortable chairs with a rectangular table. Magazines fanned out across the tabletop. A magazine from the center of the pile caught my eye, a women's magazine. I saw nothing special about it but I felt an impulse to read it. Following my inclination, I casually picked it up off the table. I am not a magazine reader and had brought a book to read. I hesitated, and started to put the magazine down, but then I stopped and randomly opened it up to a feature article. I looked up to see if my daughter noticed what I was doing, and felt a little silly until I read the article. It was about a woman who had experienced severe skin cancer on her face and scalp. She described the lesions, their seriousness and the procedure to remove them.

As I read the article, I shuddered. Chills ran up and down my spine, a sign from my body to pay attention. I carefully read every word of the article. Then I read it again. I thought about the top of my head, and the large, bloody sore that had appeared while I was in Houston. I did not know what it was, and I could not seem to get it to heal no matter what I did. From reading this article, I knew that it was skin cancer. I felt disheartened. This woman had covered herself up to avoid the sun, but still she developed skin cancer regularly. Because of my fair skin, I am careful about my sun exposure, and I usually wear a hat. The fact that I might have skin cancer had never even crossed my mind until that moment. I said nothing to my daughter about what I had read.

Armed with this newfound knowledge, I felt that my daughter's brief appointment seemed to drag on forever. I felt relieved when we could finally go home. I kept thinking about the spot on top of my head. When I got home, I took out the phone book and found a dermatology practice. I called and shared my story with the nurse about how I had randomly found the article about skin cancer, and how it had dawned on me that I had a lesion the size of a dime on top of my head. She quickly scheduled an appointment for later that week.

I did not feel upset or panicked. Instead, I felt a sense of immense gratitude for the events that had led me to my discovery. I was glad that I had paid attention, and followed through with my impulse to read the magazine that day in the orthodontist's office. I had often experienced synchronicities that made life more helpful, magical and fun. I saw this as just another puzzle piece that I needed in my quest to resolve my health. Still, I wondered how anyone who took such good care of herself could have so many different problems.

The dermatologist confirmed that I had a squamous cell carcinoma, a common type of skin cancer that develops in the outer layers of the skin. We talked about my health history. I asked if CFS and the EBV could make someone more susceptible to skin cancer. He replied that certainly people with compromised immune systems could have issues, but there were other factors to consider as well.

The dermatologist said the best course of action would be to have it surgically removed. I had lost my health insurance when my husband left his job, so I opted for the doctor to freeze the lesion off to save me the expense of surgery. The nurse came in to hold my hand. The lesion was deep, having penetrated many layers of skin. I braced myself, relaxed into my breath and cleared my mind. Determined, I sat there with the intention that the lesion would be fully removed and not return. As the doctor froze off the lesion, he stopped every now and then to make sure I was okay. I squeezed the nurse's hand hard, as my body trembled with a radiating pain that burned and stung. I fought back tears and tried not to hold my breath. I was very appreciative of the doctor's compassion and skill. For the next several weeks I placed healing salves on the spot. Since then, it has not returned.

Back at home, I sat despondent on the edge of my bed. Mr. Wiggles, who was curled up at the foot, got up and shook himself off. He came over to me with his tail wagging and sat in my lap. I held him and kissed his head and burst into tears. Enough was enough! What was wrong with me? I began to wonder if unconsciously I was sabotaging myself, thinking for some reason that I did not deserve health and happiness. I seemed to go from one illness and trauma to another, despite my good intentions and all my hard work. Things just seemed to keep going wrong, to prove me right. Something had to change.

My life reached a crescendo at this point. All the symptoms that I'd had to contend with over the years, the drama from my life, Houston. And now this — the skin cancer on top of my head — this was the tipping point for me. It was the proverbial straw that broke the camel's back.

All these years I had been as good-natured as I possibly could be. I lived in my body with my mental, emotional and physical pain, sitting quietly with it, and tried to understand why I was sick. My desire to know my body and why it had betrayed me by not getting well, despite all that I was doing, reached a level of urgency. My life had become too painful to ignore what had gone wrong. There was no more sweeping anything under the rug. It was apparent that the way I conducted my life was not giving me the results I wanted. I had hit a brick wall, so to speak. There was nothing more I could do, but just let go and remain open for something else. I had finally hit rock bottom.

I did not give up wanting to experience wellness. I did not stop asking questions and searching for answers to my health issues. But I realized that I had to focus more of my attention on anticipating the answer. I also needed to let go of the need to impose my will on my body. I was so busy taking action: researching, doing cleanses, changing my diet, doing whatever natural-health therapy I thought was worth trying, that I had neglected to be quiet. I had forgotten to tune into my body and sense what it wanted and needed. It dawned on me that I had been problem oriented, rather than solution oriented. I'd been focused on getting rid of the symptoms. I began to see that there was a big difference. At that point, I was too tired to fight any longer. Besides, it was not getting me anywhere. It was time to make peace with where I was at that moment in my life. My body was not the enemy. I needed to create a real partnership with it, to stop judging, and to stop being so critical.

I sat quietly with myself in order to notice what was going on in my body. I just sat with my symptoms, watching and feeling them, with no agenda. Then I surprised myself by feeling a sense of compassion, which morphed into a deep sense of appreciation for my body. I continued to spend time each day just being fully present, both with and for myself.

Late one afternoon, while weeding in the back yard with the Wiggs, I took a moment to look up and admire the walls of the canyon, off in the distance. The setting sun cast shadows on the rocks, heightening their red-orange colors. It was breathtakingly beautiful. At this exact moment, the thought popped into my mind that I could ask my body what it wanted and needed. I could ask my body if it knew what was making it so sick! Maybe I would get the answer I had searched for throughout these last thirty years. It was a defining moment when I suddenly comprehended that in order to hear the answer, I had to stop looking at my body as having done something wrong. I put down my shovel and sighed deeply. I felt something release in my chest, as a cool sensation flowed through my back. As I knelt in the red dirt, watching the sun slip behind the red rocks in the distance, a profound sense of peace spilled over me. I had finally and completely let go.

Chapter 16

You are not a healthy person unless you have good oral health. Oral health is part of general health and it can affect your overall health and your quality of life.

C. Everett Koop

I did not receive any answers to my health dilemma over the next several days. Then one morning out of the blue, as I walked the Wiggs, I thought of my naturopathic doctor who had become a good friend. I had not seen her since I returned from Houston, and I thought it would be fun to go and visit with her. When we met, she was alarmed by the state of my health and how exhausted and defeated I looked. She urged me to make an appointment with her colleague, a doctor who had been trained in Germany. I really had no interest in seeing yet another doctor. But over the next few days, her suggestion continued to nag at my mind. I finally called the medical consultant. After I made the appointment, I felt an unusual sense of relief move through my body. I became so hopeful, and so excited, that I could barely sleep the night before the appointment.

After telling her my story, I answered all the usual questions that I am asked during a medical exam. But this medical consultant asked me an odd question that got my attention. She inquired about my mouth, asking what kind of dental work had been done over the years. No other doctor had ever asked me about my mouth or teeth before. I told her that I'd had my wisdom teeth extracted when I was twenty, my five mercury fillings from my childhood removed in my late thirties, and two root canals performed in my forties. Without missing a beat, she suggested that my dental work could be the cause of my health issues, or could at least be contributing to them.

During my PhD course work, I had come across the work of Dr. Reinhold Voll, the German physician. In the 1940s, Dr. Voll found a way to measure the energy from acupuncture points on the skin with an ohmmeter, an instrument that measures electrical resistance. His research established a connection between parts of the body through an invisible network called meridians. According to Chinese medicine, meridians are pathways through which energy, or Qi, the life force, flows in order to maintain health. It was Dr. Voll who discovered that a tooth (which is a living organ, possessing its own nerves, blood supply and lymphatic system) could interfere with and affect the health of the body along that specific meridian. Dr. Voll found that it worked both ways: the body could affect a tooth and a tooth could affect the body. Dr. Voll's forty years of research led him to conclude that eighty percent of all illness is related to problems in the mouth.

Could my mouth be related to my health issues?

I literally felt the earth shift underneath my feet. Just as with the skin cancer on top of my head, chills ran up and down my spine, while a pleasant feeling of warmth spread throughout my body. I held my breath as the medical consultant handed me the card of a biological dentist who practiced integrative medicine. In that very moment, I felt the muscles in my shoulders release and relax; the weight of my burdens seemed to melt away. Instinctively, I knew that I needed to see this dentist. I needed to explore the link between my mouth, with all the dental work in it, and my health. Maybe this time I would get to the root cause.

The medical consultant explained that biological dentists think holistically. She told me that they understood that the health of the mouth is an integral part of overall health. Biological dentistry is concerned with the elimination of infection and works with the body's natural ability to heal. A biological dentist combines both modern dental diagnostics and treatments with integrative medicine and natural approaches. The biological dentist to whom she referred me would work to find solutions to my dental issues, in ways that would be well suited to my body and support my overall health and well-being.

Biological dentists use materials that are uniquely compatible with each patient's body. They do not use fluoride or mercury. They are careful to test their patients for compatibility with dental materials that could potentially cause allergic reactions, and contribute to illness and disease. They have developed protocols that differ from those of conventional dentistry. These protocols minimize the chance of causing serious long-term health problems.

I was not sure how my dental health might relate to my problems, but I was open to discovering the answers. I was now fifty-one years old, and hopeful that this next chapter of my life would no longer include health issues. My health had taken a great deal of my time, focus and money. It had influenced the decisions I made about everything: what I ate, what I would do and where I would go. I had to plan my life around the limitations imposed by how I felt, or how I thought I might feel. I knew that I had missed out on a lot of friendships, opportunities and good times.

On the other hand, my health issues had made me explore more deeply who I really am, and caused me to look at life from a broader perspective. My challenges forced me to make conscious choices daily about how I wanted to feel and respond. My health limitations made me prioritize everything in my life, including my beliefs and values, and consider what was worth keeping and what was not. Most importantly, these experiences afforded me the opportunity to become authentic. I took nothing for granted. I had taken responsibility for my life and my well-being, my thoughts, words and deeds.

Chapter 17

The price of anything is the amount of life you exchange for it.

Henry David Thoreau

It took me a couple of weeks to get the nerve to call and make an appointment with the biological dentist. Why so long? I do not know. Perhaps I procrastinated because I was afraid that I would just hit another dead end in resolving my health issues. But when I finally did make the appointment, I was so happy that I could have danced a jig, and I did. I began to share with my family and friends that I had an appointment with a biological dentist who might help me clear up my health issues. I would first encounter silence, and then they would roll their eyes and sigh. The gist of what they said was that my mouth and dental work could not possibly have anything to do with my overall health. They thought I was on another wild goose chase. They were wrong.

When I went for my new-patient exam at the biological dentist's office, I was both nervous and excited. The biological dentist performed several different tests to determine the health of my mouth, some of which were unfamiliar to me. I had entered a whole new world in that office, a world of new possibilities that I never knew existed. I learned a new vocabulary during my appointment. I had my blood drawn for a test that would check my body's compatibility with different dental materials.

I asked the dentist how he came to practice biological dentistry. He told me two stories. One was about an amalgam dental filling with mercury that he had placed in a twelve-year-old girl's mouth. Several weeks later the girl's left eye started to twitch. Her eye doctor and neurologist found nothing wrong; the girl and her mother returned to see if the mercury in the filling had caused the problem. My dentist said that he had called the American Dental Association, and they told him that could never happen. He ended up removing the amalgam filling — and the girl's eye stopped twitching almost immediately. He told me he realized that mercury, which makes up 50% of an amalgam filling, is an extremely toxic metal and does not belong in the human body.

My biological dentist then shared his second experience with me. A tow truck hit the car he was driving. Unbeknownst to him, the accident had caused serious stress on his body. He developed temporomandibular joint disorder (TMJ); his neck swelled; he developed bad indigestion and gas, along with kidney stones. The doctors diagnosed him with thyroid cancer and removed his thyroid. The biopsy report showed that his thyroid was normal. He saw a meridian tooth chart and realized that the root canal he'd had, on tooth #3, corresponded to the thyroid. After having the root canal removed, all his symptoms vanished. Except now, due to his medical treatments, he was diabetic.

As we put together a treatment plan for my dental issues, I learned that each of the four extraction sites from my wisdom teeth had "cavitations," or holes, in the jawbone, where the bone had died after the extractions. We also found cavitations at the tips of my two root canals. Could these issues really be causing my health problems? Was it so far fetched to think that my mouth had anything to do with my health? I had always been told that I had a healthy mouth. Now I realized that this was just not the case. I handed the dentist a list I had brought of most of the health symptoms I'd endured. It was hard to tell that I had taken such good care of myself by the numerous symptoms I listed. I told him that, for whatever reason, I could not seem to make headway on getting rid of my symptoms. I was frustrated and hopeful that this promising new dentist could shed some light on the situation.

1. Low energy, exhaustion
2. Indigestion, gas, bloating, constipation
3. Swollen liver, crampy and scratchy sensations, heat sensations
4. Hypoglycemia
5. Hypothyroidism, adrenal fatigue, brain fog, memory loss
6. Hormonal imbalance, inability to shed weight
7. Panic/anxiety attacks
8. Arthritis in right hand
9. Inability to sleep through the night, unrefreshing sleep
10. Unable to stay hydrated
11. Urinary tract infections
12. Respiratory infections, bronchitis, bacterial pneumonia
13. Chronic fatigue syndrome, Epstein-Barr virus
14. Swollen lymph nodes, worse on right side of the body, neck
15. Easily get sick, hard to recover
16. Astigmatism, right eye

17. Plantar warts, constantly getting them
18. Skin rashes, hives, muscle pain, stiffness, swelling
19. Inability to smell, stuffy nose
20. Bad breath
21. Low blood pressure

As he looked at the list, he told me that all cavitations and root canals are infected with bacteria, which can interfere with the proper functioning of the body. He went on to tell me that infections in the mouth can cause or contribute to illness in other areas of the body, which are called focal infections. After each surgery, biopsies of the sites are sent to a pathology lab. A report that identifies and describes the bacteria found in the lesions is sent back after a few weeks. These biopsies usually show harmful bacteria, viruses and/or fungi.

I felt the warmth and softness of chills move up and down my spine as we talked. The pleasant sensations made me feel hopeful. I realized that I would have to wait and see what improvements I would have as a result of the surgeries.

There are as many as seventy-two different names to describe cavitations, including "ischemic osteonecrosis." "Ischemic" means inadequate blood flow, "osteo" means bone and "necrosis" means dead. Ischemic osteonecrosis can affect any bone in the body, such as the hip, shin or knee, but biological dentists have found this condition to be most common in the jawbone. Cavitations in the jawbone are now commonly referred to as Neuralgia-Inducing Cavitational Osteonecrosis (NICO). NICO, the dentist told me, is a misnomer, because often there is no pain (neuralgia) or inflammation associated with these lesions. Because of the lack of pain, they are often not discovered.

I nodded and told him that I'd never had pain in my jawbone. I wanted to know why cavitations form.

Cavitations can happen naturally, he said; the third molars (wisdom teeth) are a good example. When the tooth erupts naturally through the gum, the jawbone around it dissolves to allow the tooth to surface. If the tooth is impacted, both the bone and tooth will become infected and die. The infection can actually block the blood supply from getting through the bone. Bone marrow edema can be another cause of tissue death as well. Marrow is a fatty substance in the bone that produces red blood cells. When the bone marrow is swollen, blood flow can get into the area, but not out of it.

There are several other reasons why cavitations form: blood disorders, hormonal imbalances, poor nutrition, smoking, stress, or accident. Bisphosphonate drugs that are used to slow down bone damage have several side effects, one being osteonecrosis of the jawbone. In other words, anyone can have cavitations. My biological dentist said that the number-one cause of cavitations is the way teeth are extracted. More often than not, patients end up with cavitations. Curious, I asked him what he meant.

He explained to me that many oral surgeons and dentists use epinephrine (which is the same as adrenaline) with their anesthetic when they numb the area. Epinephrine is used as a convenience during surgery to restrict blood flow. This means there are no red blood cells to deliver oxygen to the area. Without oxygen, the bone cells die quickly, ensuring that the area will not heal. It is important that the socket be allowed to bleed so that a good clot can form, which is needed to grow new, healthy bone.

My biological dentist also shared with me that often the periodontal ligament is not removed from the extraction site. I looked puzzled, so he explained that a periodontal ligament holds each tooth in place in the jawbone. (Fig. 5) The ligament runs around the submerged part of the tooth, as well as its roots. It acts as a shock absorber, so that the tooth does not rub against the jawbone when pressure is applied. The periodontal ligament also ensures that the tooth remains separate from the jawbone and prohibits additional bone growth in the socket. Wisdom teeth are enclosed in a fluid-filled sac that is used to create the periodontal ligament as they grow. Dentists and oral surgeons do not remove the sac or the periodontal ligament. They reason that the body will break it down over time.

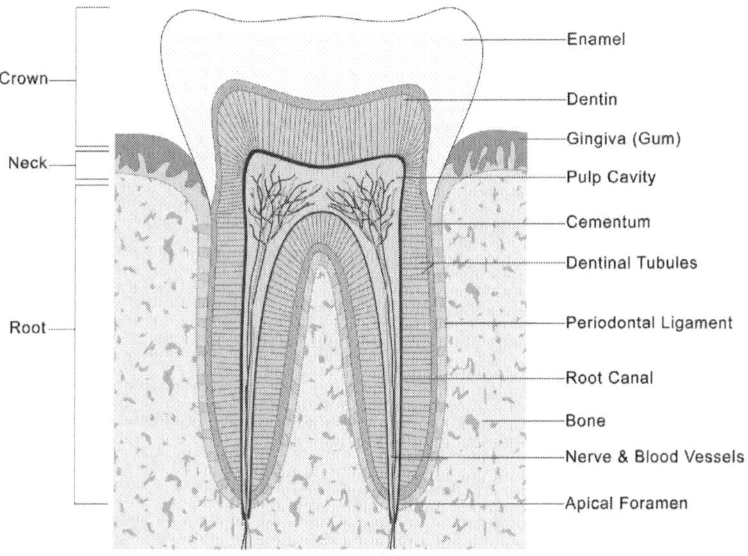

Fig. 5 Anatomy of a tooth.

He explained that as the sac and/or ligament deteriorate, the body thinks that the tooth is still there. Because of this, the jawbone does not heal. New bone will not fill in the extraction site, since the ligament is a biological barrier to such growth. Sometimes when a tooth is extracted, a portion of the ligament will come out with the tooth. This is why cavitations come in so many shapes and sizes. Since the periodontal ligament does not reach to the top of the socket, a thin, boney cap can form over the extraction site, which gives the illusion that new bone has formed throughout.

I leaned forward, fascinated by what I was learning. He continued, the boney cap traps the bacteria and other microorganisms within the socket. With lack of oxygen and damaged tissue, a chronic infection develops at the site. I nodded again as I carefully listened. Usually, both the extracted tooth and the jawbone underneath the periodontal ligament are infected. That area of the jawbone dies and resembles gangrene. The trapped bacteria and their toxic waste create a cesspool in the unhealed, necrotic socket of the extracted tooth. The toxicity found in cavitations and root canals are pretty much the same. The damage to the body seems to be cumulative. As the bacteria and its toxins travel from the mouth, a secondary infection known as a focal infection can occur in weakened parts of the body, and over time can raise the risk of illness.

I asked him what kinds of illness a focal infection from the mouth could create. He answered that there could be many different kinds, depending on genetics, body weaknesses, the meridian the tooth lies on and the type of bacteria. Some examples are: chronic fatigue syndrome, heart disease, fibromyalgia, arthritis, digestive problems and even cancers. Some people's immune systems can handle the toxicity, some cannot. But after a while, the body becomes overloaded with toxins and stress — the body can only deal with so much.

He explained to me that cavitations often do not just stay in one place, and can create tunnels to other teeth. The gangrene can spread. The patient can end up with another cavitation, or perhaps a new root canal, and then the cycle of infection begins again — which creates more risk of symptoms in other parts of the body. I shuddered as I thought about this scenario. This all made perfect sense to me. Based on my experiences, I now understood that dentists and doctors knew nothing at all about cavitations in the jawbone. Why was this not being discussed? Why did people not know that focal infections that originated in the mouth could cause illness and disease throughout the body? I had no idea that dental work had such far-reaching effects on overall health.

Amazed at what I had just learned, I sat back in my chair. My mind raced to connect all the dots from my health odyssey. Was this my holy grail? Was this really the answer I had searched for — and was this, finally, the root cause of the symptoms I had suffered with for thirty years? I was ready to find out. I closed my eyes and took a deep breath, emptying the air out of my lungs slowly, with an audible sigh. Everything disappeared into the darkness as my awareness shifted to deep inside myself. This meeting was a defining moment in my life. I stood on the edge of some discovery. I sighed again and shifted my weight in the chair. I needed a moment to absorb the information that the biological dentist had just shared with me. This was the first I had ever heard of cavitations in the mouth and focal infections.

I had never thought about my wisdom tooth extractions or root canal procedures as having anything to do with my overall health. In fact, I guess I never really gave much thought to my mouth at all, except when I brushed or flossed my teeth or had dental checkups. The only thing I knew about teeth was the direct link between nutrition and the mouth. I had read a book by dentist Weston A. Price entitled

Nutrition and Physical Degeneration (1938) several years before, when I was studying nutrition for my certifications.

Dr. Price had visited eleven countries to study the mouths of indigenous people who still ate their healthy native diets. These people were free of cavities and dental-arch deformities, and had no crooked teeth. He observed that they were extraordinarily healthy. I remembered that he had included many photos in his book. The x-ray photos of cavities from one of his patients made a real impression upon me. The photos showed new growth of the dentin (the hard, boney tissue underneath the enamel which makes up the bulk of the tooth) that had been eaten away by the cavities! The teenage girl had followed Dr. Price's nutritional guidelines, which had allowed the cavities to heal.[14]

I thought about the amalgam fillings, which I'd had removed years before, because I understood that mercury was a toxic substance. At that point, I thought my mouth was completely healthy. I then recalled that Dr. Price's son Donald had a root canal performed by his father. Donald died of complications from that infected tooth. As a result, for twenty-five years, Dr. Price went on to study, research and treat the problems associated with dental infections caused by root canals.

I cleared my throat and touched the heart pendant that hung around my neck. I opened my eyes and smiled. I felt peaceful and calm, which was an excellent sign. I had a very good feeling about going ahead with these surgeries, which are referred to as dental revisions, to clean out my mouth. It was then that I realized I would need to take a leap of faith and "boldly go into the great and vast unknown" of experience that most people did not know even existed. I would need to take this journey alone, knowing that there was a lot of controversy surrounding the subject of dentistry and its relationship to over-all health. What Dr. Price wrote in his books on dental infections sums up the "unprecedented antagonism" that these ideas and professionals still encounter today:

> *"I wish to express my deep indebtedness to all these pioneers in this field; if my work shall have removed some of the confusions which have been largely responsible for the lack of appreciation, and opposition to, the efforts of these great pioneers, I should be doubly glad because of my esteem for their courage in the midst of the bitterest opposition, and also for the larger helpfulness that may come to humanity..."*[15]

I had nothing to lose — and everything to gain.

Chapter 18

Physical pathology is therefore the result of disease, not the cause.

Samuel Hahnemann

The day finally arrived for my first surgery. I had waited over thirty years for this moment. I was about to undergo a specialized surgery that is not generally known or accepted. I was out on the leading edge, ready and excited to see what would happen. I knew with every bone in my body that this surgery was the right course of action. I was hopeful that my health would improve in many ways. How? I did not know, but I knew that this was the answer. I knew for certain that the surgeries would diminish the overall toxic load in my body. It made perfect sense to me that this would take the edge off the stress on my immune system, and allow my body to heal. I was hopeful that I had found the root cause of the chronic fatigue symptoms and other issues.

I had told my dentist that I wanted him first to clean out the two cavitations on the right side of my mouth. It was here that the lymph nodes in my neck were the most swollen and sore. I impatiently waited for the surgery to begin. As the dental assistant prepped me, my anticipation grew. The dentist drew a sample of my blood and placed it into a machine called a centrifuge that would spin and separate it into its different component parts. We would place the plasma-rich fibrin from my blood sample into the cleaned-out extraction sites. Using my body's own healing mechanism would help to form healthy blood clots and encourage new bone growth.

I chose to use a unique option offered by my biological dentist to make the surgery less stressful. This system, developed by neuroscientists, naturally creates the relaxation response of the mind and body in minutes for an anxiety-free dental procedure. My dentist's assistant gave me orange-flavored supplements to promote relaxation. Microcurrent patches were then placed behind my ears to keep me in a relaxed state during the surgery. I put on headphones that played beautiful, calming classical music that entrains brainwaves. I felt very relaxed, as if I was ready to fall asleep. The assistant handed me a pair of dark glasses. I yawned as I put them on.

My thoughts floated back to the day I had my wisdom teeth removed. I remembered sitting in a small waiting room with a strong antiseptic smell and white-and-pale-blue textured wallpaper. As I got up to follow the nurse, my mom squeezed my hand, smiled at me, and told me I would do just fine.

A few moments later, my biological dentist gave me injections to numb the areas he was about to open and clean out, removing the infections so that my jawbone could finally heal. I heard his voice quietly say something to his assistant as he waited for the area to numb. I could feel the chain that hung around my neck, with the heart pendant touching my skin. I focused on the necklace for a moment. The inscription on the back — "Boldly go into the great and vast unknown" — echoed in my mind. I felt reassured.

My biological dentist interrupted my thoughts to announce that it was time to begin. As I opened my mouth wide, he placed a block between my upper and lower teeth to hold my jaw open. He started with the upper-right cavitation. As he opened the gum and broke through the thin, boney cap that had formed at the top of the extraction site, he found a hole in the jawbone — the cavitation. Inside the cavitation he discovered a "medicament." A medicament is a dressing used to protect the blood clot that forms after the extraction of a tooth to discourage "dry socket."

Dry socket is a painful condition that happens when a blood clot does not properly form, or dissolves before healing is complete. Over thirty years ago, the oral surgeon had placed this dressing into the extraction site of my wisdom tooth to prevent dry socket. That medicament now consisted of gray, translucent globules. My biological dentist removed the offending medicament and cleaned out the socket. He scraped away a millimeter of the bone until he saw fresh blood pooling from the newly revealed healthy bone. Next, he irrigated the site with a homeopathic solution and placed the centrifuged fibrin from my own blood into the socket. Now, with the medicament out of the extraction site and the infection removed, a robust blood clot would form, and new, healthy bone could finally grow to fill in the hole.

I sat quietly, comfortably drifting in and out as I listened to the music from the headphones. I started to pay closer attention to my dentist and his assistant, as they got ready to work on the bottom cavitation. When the dentist began to open the bottom gum, I felt something stir deep in my gut, something so deep inside that I was taken aback. A warm, soft, swirling sensation rhythmically moved throughout my body. It felt playful and happy as it gently surfaced. My abdomen started to tremor, as a quiet cry of delight vibrated through me. Then, to my amazement, tears of joy started to stream down my face and continued throughout the rest of the surgery. I lay there in awe as I watched a part of me — a part that had been buried alive for the majority of my life — express emotion and gratitude. I was engulfed in a feeling of joy and appreciation that I cannot even begin to describe. It was an experience that I will always remember.

As the dentist looked into the lower cavitation site, he found not only a medicament but also a surprise that he had not seen before: the cavitation was actively releasing pus and infection. As he told me afterward, "It was spewing!" For the past thirty years, the medicament in that socket had been creating a geyser of irritation and infection. The inflammation process in my jawbone had desperately tried to break down the offending foreign object in the extraction site, an object that could not be destroyed. To clean out the medicament, he again had to extract the gray, translucent globules. The dentist said it was the worst mess he had ever seen. My body had tried, over time, to break down and rid itself of this substance, but it was impossible. With the medicament still in place, the site was unable to heal. The infected bone had died, leaving behind a hidden crater of misery in my mouth.

As the dentist and his assistant completed the cavitation surgery, I felt a new, and very odd sensation in my neck. It was very subtle. The dense feeling of discomfort I had felt for many years had completely disappeared. It dawned on me that the lymph in my neck had finally released. The lumpiness and accompanying achiness were gone! My husband was right; my lymph had been doing its job all along — protecting my body from what was in the wisdom tooth socket. With the cavitations cleaned out, and no longer spewing infection, there was no need for my lymph to respond in that manner.

The exhaustion that had become my body's normal condition since my twenties began to melt away. The weight lifted from me. My whole body sighed with relief. I felt like a different person. If that was not gift enough, directly after the surgery I noticed that the arthritis in my right hand was gone! There was no swelling in my joints, and there was no pain. I could now wear my favorite dolphin ring again. I was beside myself with excitement. I could barely contain myself when the dentist brought my husband into the room. I had everyone feel my neck and look at my hand.

Following the surgery, I placed a homeopathic lotion on my cheek and neck to reduce the pain and swelling. The assistant moved me to another room and made me comfortable, and shone an anodyne light on the area where the surgery had just been completed. The assistant explained to me that the infrared light therapy would help to reduce pain and swelling. It also increased blood circulation, which is very important in the overall healing of the sites. My husband sat next to me and held my hand — now arthritis free! I felt victorious and relieved. My tears dried up, and I drifted in and out of a deep and peaceful sleep.

Chapter 19

It's not a miracle that the body heals. The miracle is that we survive after all that is done to the body.

Marc Viafora

Those first few nights after my first surgery were the first time in years that I slept peacefully through the night. The severe exhaustion was gone, but initially I tired easily. I continued with my therapeutic regimen to assist my body in its healing process. I stayed in bed for the next three days and took care of myself. For the first time in my life, I made myself a priority and put me first. I listened carefully to what my body told me, and I continued to follow my intuition and instincts as best I could. I was now able to identify my needs and communicate them to others in more authentic, heartfelt ways that felt satisfying. It was easier to set boundaries with people and to say no. I felt in charge of my life — and it was really fun. My first surgery left me empowered.

As weeks progressed, focusing became easier. In my new state of awareness, I began to look around me and feel a deeper connection with my home, and with the beauty of Sedona, in a way I had never experienced before. I had clarity and insight. I had enough energy to do the small things in life, such as fold the laundry, organize a closet and be fully present in conversations with friends and family. Life became richer, more beautiful and more gratifying. I started to appreciate the people in my life much more. Most importantly, I appreciated myself. I was in awe of the healing capabilities of my body. I felt grounded, happy and hopeful.

When I walked Wiggles again, my neighbors did not recognize me from a distance. I was no longer slumped over or moving slowly. I stood tall, and I confidently stepped forward with an energetic, purposeful gait. The light in my eyes was back, and I was animated. Every day, I counted my blessings and looked for things to appreciate — and I found them in abundance.

When the pathology report (Appendix A) came back from the first dental surgery, it confirmed a NICO (Neuralgia Inducing Cavitational Osteonecrosis) diagnosis, with crystallized bone and fatty tissue, caused by an infection in the bone. The medicament (dressing) that long ago had been placed into the surgical sites of both the upper and lower wisdom tooth extractions had created a "myospherulosis" response. A myospherulosis is a type of granuloma caused by a foreign body, and a granuloma is an inflammatory reaction that occurs when the immune system tries to contain a foreign substance it cannot eliminate.

With my eyes closed, my mind wandered back to the oral surgeon's office where I'd had my wisdom teeth extracted when I was twenty. I could remember what was running through my mind that day: thoughts of school, my friends and all the courses I wanted to take. The laughing gas made me relaxed, but it had not diminished my excitement about everything I wanted to accomplish. I recall feeling relieved when the surgery was over. Oddly enough, I clearly remembered the oral surgeon telling me that he was going to place an antibiotic in these two sites that would help the sockets heal. I knew he had not placed them in the other side, and I was now very grateful for that.

I learned from my biological dentist that the medicament was tetracycline powder in a petroleum-based carrier, a semisolid mixture of petroleum hydrocarbons. This was a popular dressing, back when I had my wisdom teeth extracted. In the Journal of Oral Maxillofacial Surgery (1990), I found an article that explained that these insoluble tetracycline preparations cause irritation of the tissues in the socket, since the tetracycline cannot break down, and the petroleum-based carrier will further intensify that reaction.[16]

Petroleum carriers interfere with the healing of the extraction site and can even cause soft-tissue tumors. In addition, people can be allergic to both the tetracycline and petroleum. The carrier is also a breeding ground for infection, as it was in my case, and can create what is commonly called a "foreign-body giant cell reaction."[17] The infection and pus that spewed from my cavitations had created chronic inflammation in the sockets, and never allowed them to heal. My immune system could not break down either the tetracycline or its petroleum-based medicament.

Some dentists and oral surgeons use medicaments after a tooth extraction in the hopes of preventing painful dry socket, in which the blood clot that forms in the extraction site — which protects the exposed bone and nerve endings in the socket — dislodges and dissolves before healing is completed. There are many theories as to why dry sockets happen, which include trauma from the surgery or existing inflammation in the jawbone or adjacent tissues.[18]

Practitioners have their own protocol and favorite medicament (if they use them) to prevent dry socket. In general, the articles I read suggested that medicaments have side effects, can cause allergic reactions and can delay the healing process. They are foreign matter that dentists place into the socket, which must then be broken down and absorbed by the body.[19] I had learned from my biological dentist that with any infected or impacted tooth, there is always an existing infection in the jawbone. I wondered if any kind of medicament could be broken down and absorbed by the body if the infection was not removed at the time of the surgery. I asked a dentist who is well versed in this subject that exact question. He responded that if the jawbone had an infection present in that specific extraction site, and a medicament was placed into it, the result would be "a real mess."

I also received a report from Fry Laboratories that listed the bacteria found in the lower right cavitation. The lab tests for bacteria that consist of 1% or more of the sample. My biopsy contained three different kinds of bacteria — each of which can cause pneumonia, an illness I had struggled with repeatedly throughout my adulthood! Two of these were Neisseria, which are normally found in the upper respiratory tract and the back of the mouth. Neisseria lactamica comprised 88.87% of the sample and Neisseria flavescens comprised 4.92% of the sample. Neisseria lactamica and flavescens can both cause bacterial pneumonia and septicemia (blood poisoning) in immune-compromised individuals. The third type of bacteria was Streptococcus pneumoniae (1.02%), which also causes pneumonia. (Appendix A)

Different doctors over the years told me not to worry about toxins or bacteria: my immune system would take care of these invaders. But from personal experience, I knew what happens when the immune system is overburdened and compromised. The body cannot efficiently or effectively fight infections, viruses or illnesses of any kind, as its ability to heal is impaired. Dr. Weston Price found that patients with focal infections from cavitations and root canals healed more slowly than those who did not. I had experienced this phenomenon frequently with flus, colds, and viruses. It took me two-and-a-half years to recover from pneumonia when I first moved to Arizona. Dr. George E. Meinig commented in his book, *Root Canal Cover-Up,* that when the immune system is overtaxed for long periods of time by hidden focal infections and their toxins, "Such people more readily develop pneumonia or some other affliction, which eventually causes their deaths." [20]

Chapter 20

The truth is you don't know what is going to happen tomorrow. Life is a crazy ride, and nothing is guaranteed.

Eminem

It was time to get ready for bed. I rubbed Wiggles's stomach as he stretched out on his back next to me. We watched the night sky from my porch. I pondered over a dream I'd had earlier that morning. I tried to remember what it was about, but could recall only bits and pieces. I knew that the poster of Princess Bia from my college dorm room was in the dream. Poor little Bia was still trapped in the box, but her red rubber ball had mysteriously moved closer to her hand. I saw it as a good omen — Bia's small ball now within her reach confirmed that I was indeed on the right path to reclaim my health and my life. The ball continued to represent my creativity, clarity and vitality, which had now started to emerge thanks to the partial removal of the constant flow of toxins from my mouth into the rest of my body.

Six weeks had passed since my first surgery. My energy was higher than it had been in a long time. I no longer needed to nap in the afternoon; the feeling of overwhelm was gone. I felt clearer overall. My nutritional and stress-management consulting business picked up, and I started to enjoy my work again. I also felt well enough to make plans, to socialize and to go out with my girlfriends. My husband and I took our first hike since my surgery. Afterwards, I was not wiped out and headachy for the rest of the day! I had a new lease on life. In the morning I would wake up and actually feel excited about the day ahead. Even my two daughters noticed positive changes in their mom. I felt happy and satisfied.

I stretched and absent-mindedly yawned as I looked up into the expansive night sky and searched for shooting stars. I shifted my thoughts back to Bia. Her drawer, still partially opened in my dream, did not reveal any of its contents. There seemed to be a correlation between that drawer, my mouth and specifically my jawbone. Only by fully opening each of them, would a trove of hidden secrets be exposed. I looked down at Wiggles, who got up and moved to the far side of the love seat we shared. I smiled at him. Wiggles lay down, curled up in a ball and looked up at me. It was good to be with the Wiggs, my loyal friend and constant companion. I reached over to pet him.

It had been quite a day. That morning I had taken Wiggs to the veterinarian to have his teeth cleaned for the first time. I was a little nervous about the whole thing and asked her many questions. I went home and impatiently waited for the phone call from the office to pick him up. I felt restless. Her assistant finally called to tell me that everything had gone well. They had pulled one tooth that was badly cracked. My mind focused on the phrase "pulled one tooth." I was horrified. My heart pounded so hard and fast, I thought it would tear my chest open. "She did what?" I yelled into the phone. The assistant must have thought I'd over-reacted, but I had good reason. I said I would come right over, and that I wanted to meet with the veterinarian.

I hit every red light on the way to the office. I took deep breaths and told myself that everything would be just fine. After I parked the car, I ran into the office, car keys still in my hand. The administrative staff had obviously been told that Wiggles's mom needed to see the vet right away. Everyone wanted to know what the urgency was all about. The veterinarian calmly walked into the waiting area to see what I needed. Words tumbled out of me. I was not sure that what I said made any sense; I felt frantic. She smiled and told me that in veterinary school she was taught to remove the periodontal ligament when extracting a tooth so the jawbone would heal properly. I looked at her with a mix of relief and disbelief. "So the periodontal ligament is removed with the tooth?" "Yes," she replied. "We want to make sure that the socket is empty and clean."

I explained to her that many dentists do not remove the periodontal ligament, which my biological dentist had told me creates an obstacle to healing the socket. From my personal experience, I realized the dying bone and periodontal ligament become a breeding ground of infection for pathogenic bacteria. I briefly explained what had happened to me when I had my wisdom teeth extracted. She told me that Wiggles was fine.

My biological dentist had told me that dentists originally did remove the periodontal ligament. His father's dental books from the 1950s had described the procedure. But that had changed with the advent of antibiotics. It is hard for me to understand why it is now okay to leave the periodontal ligament in for people, while my veterinarian was taught to remove the ligament and make sure the socket is clean for dogs. People deserve better as well.

In a few days I would undergo my second surgery. I looked forward to it and could not wait to see further improvement in my health. I continued with my health regimen to prepare myself for the big day. "Boldly go into the great and vast unknown!" I exclaimed with joy to the night sky.

My necklace rested in a dish on the nightstand by my bed. Shortly after returning from Houston, I had seen the pendant in a small shop that displayed colorful, decorative glass objects in the windows. My husband and I had been out for lunch, and we decided to stroll through the festive, colorful courtyards and small shops in Tlaquepaque. The necklace had caught my eye as we were about to leave the store. I walked over to the glass case and studied the pendant.

It had cutout shapes of a moon and stars, with intricate designs engraved on the heart-shaped pendant. I loved the small pink, green, blue and purple semiprecious stones that added a bit of color. As I held the necklace, I was delighted to find an inscription on the back that read, "Boldly go into the great and vast unknown," although it did not yet hold significance for me. After I tried it on, I hesitatingly handed it back to the woman and thanked her. I had felt at home and happy with the necklace dangling around my neck.

Over the next few days, I could not get that necklace out of my mind. I mentioned it to my husband several times. Little did I know that he had returned to the shop later that afternoon. A few weeks later, my husband presented the necklace to me as a gift.

I yawned and stretched again as I saw a shooting star flash across the sky. As I watched the star disappear I made a wish: "May I find what it is that I am to do to make the world more beautiful." I took a deep breath and inhaled the clean, crisp air. Then I stood up and reached for the Wiggs, who by now had fallen asleep. Cuddling him in my arms, I opened the sliding screen door and stepped inside to my bedroom.

Chapter 21

Citizens are not informed of the multiple disease-producing bacteria living in their root canals.

Hal A. Huggins, DDS, MS

Relaxed in the dental chair with my dark glasses on, I had been prepped for my second surgery. My headphones played beautiful, calming classical music. As in my first surgery, a microcurrent patch placed behind each of my ears would help to keep me in a relaxed state. I could taste the remnants of the orange-flavored supplements that would also help promote the relaxation response. My biological dentist and his assistant talked in the background as we waited for the anesthetic to take effect. In this second surgery, my left front tooth and incisor, which had been treated via root canal, would be removed.

When I had first moved to Sedona, I fainted and fell face down on a concrete pad. I broke my incisor tooth, which pushed the front tooth next to it out of alignment. I was devastated. Over time the two teeth slowly died. My conventional dentist urged me to have a root canal treatment, which I eventually did, because I did not know what else to do. Dentistry offers very few choices when a tooth becomes badly damaged or dies. The tooth can either be extracted or a procedure called a root canal can be done to "save the tooth."

Root canals are a standard approach in dentistry and have been around for a long time. The nerve, blood supply and lymph, which are housed in the center of the tooth (pulp chamber) and which travel down through the roots, are removed. The chamber and the two or four canals are then sterilized. A latex material called "gutta percha" is packed inside to create a seal. Sometimes a metal post is inserted in one of the canals to strengthen the weakened structure of the tooth. A crown made to resemble the tooth (which can include different metals) is placed over the lifeless form. (Fig. 6)

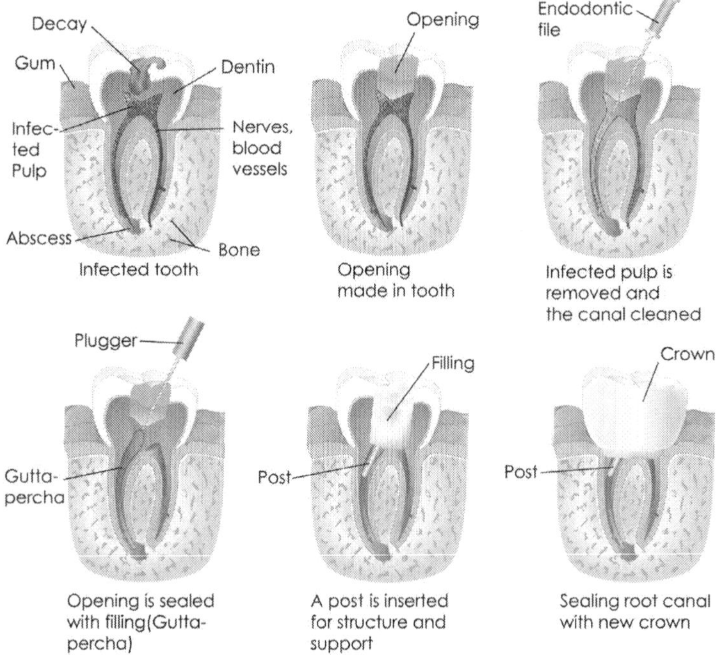

Fig. 6 Root Canal procedure.

Root canal treatment is designed to eliminate both pain and bacteria from the infected root canal and to prevent reinfection of the tooth. According to many biological dentists and those researchers before them, a root canal cannot be fully sterilized and therefore always remains infected.[21] For starters, the gutta percha used as a sealant shrinks as it dries. Bacteria can then escape around the shrunken sealant inside the tooth. The periodontal ligament, the shock absorber between the tooth and jawbone, becomes a breeding ground for these harmful bacteria. When pressure in the form of biting, chewing or grinding is applied to the tooth, bacteria and their toxins can enter the lymph system and bloodstream, travel to other parts of the body, and create or exacerbate disease and illness.[22] Over 150 different types of bacteria have been discovered which can make root canal treated teeth their home.[23]

Moreover, a tooth is not a solid structure. It has millions of microscopic channels called "tubules" that make up the dentin and carry nutrients from the center of the tooth (pulp chamber) to the enamel on the surface. Although a tooth has only one to four roots, it also has a maze of accessory canals made up of tubules. (Fig. 7) If the tubules from one of the small front lower teeth were laid out end to end, it would measure three miles long![24] Dr. Weston Price counted as many as seventy-five accessory canals in one front tooth.[25] It just is not possible to sterilize every tubule in a tooth. After the root canal procedure, the bacteria in the tubules are cut off from oxygen, nutrients and blood supply. Neither antibiotics nor the white blood cells of the immune system can enter and attack the pathogenic bacteria located there. Often the infection reaches down into the periodontal ligament and jawbone. This can create a cavitation where pathogenic bacteria can grow, along with an assortment of cysts and tumors.

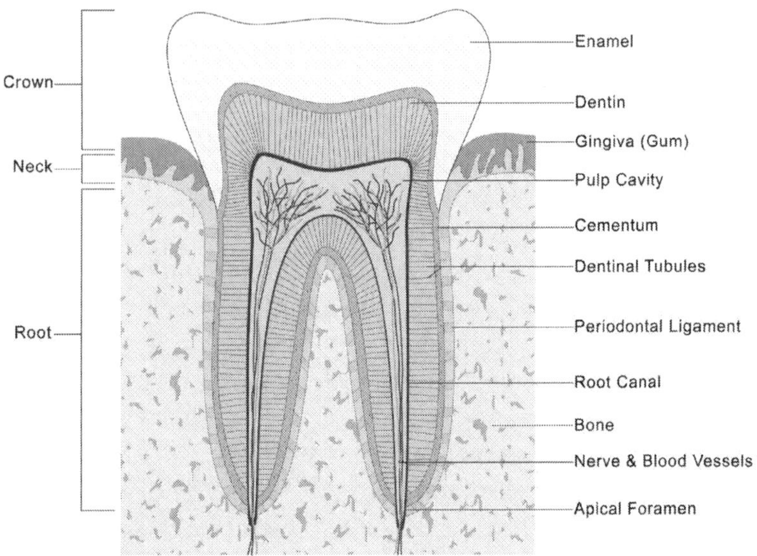

Fig. 7 Dentinal Tubules

The environment inside the tooth and the surrounding area has now been changed by the root canal procedure; the tissues are damaged and traumatized. The bacteria in the tubules respond by adapting to their new environment. They produce toxic acidic waste, which can spread to other parts of the body and create symptoms and disease. Teeth are alive; a root canal treated tooth is dead. The body does not like non-vital organs or structures. According to Dr. Hal Huggins, the body launches an autoimmune attack against the dead tooth, which can either create or increase autoimmune issues.[26]

I had cause for concern, because I was already dealing with CFS and the EB virus.

Based partly on what I'd learned about root canals and the choice I was inspired to make, I had my biological dentist remove my two root canals. Deep down, I believed that these teeth were contributing to my poor health. I wanted to reduce my overall toxic load so that my body could more easily heal.

As my morning surgery progressed, my dentist easily and expertly removed the two dead teeth. Sure enough, there was a cavitation under each tooth. The black, spongy holes in my jawbone were not empty, but filled with cysts! As the dentist cleaned out these areas, I noticed the pressure and stuffiness in my left nostril disappear. My head felt clearer. The general non-specific achiness in my body disappeared. My body again sighed with relief.

A few minutes later I had an amazing experience. I became keenly aware of my body: my toes and feet, my legs and thighs, my torso and arms, hands, neck and head. A steady pulse connected all the parts of my body together. I felt relaxed by the rhythmic flow of my breath as it moved in and out, like waves leisurely lapping on a shoreline. As a stress-management and nutrition consultant, I have always thought that I was in touch with my body, but this was beyond anything I had ever experienced. I was almost giddy. This connection felt grounding and reassuring. It dawned on me that much of the time I really did not inhabit my body. I tried to ignore it, since my symptoms made living there uncomfortable. As the dentist sewed up the extraction sites, it felt good to be fully present again.

I enjoyed my new discovery, and sensed that I had connected with something even greater. I felt full and at peace. Every cell of my body resonated with a joyful and playful sensation that felt familiar, yet foreign, at the same time. I felt so alive in that moment. I tuned into this soft and gentle feeling. It made me feel at home within myself in a way that I had not known for a long time. I took a deep breath and sighed with happiness.

As the dentist finished, I turned my attention to the pendant that hung from the chain around my neck. I thought of the inscription, "Boldly go into the great and vast unknown." During this surgery, I had profoundly explored the connection with my body in a totally unexpected way. I found myself intimately in relationship with something far greater, which I had only dreamed of achieving in my yoga or meditation practice. I felt humble and grateful.

My dental surgeries served an even greater purpose than to clean the pathogenic bacteria, which had stressed and compromised my health and well-being, out of my mouth. Each surgery was like peeling an onion. One by one, the layers of years of self-criticism, disappointment and disillusionment were removed. This was a rite of passage. I felt a tremendous sense of self-forgiveness, love and peace. The surgeries cleared out the clutter and static not only in my mouth, but also in my life. The exhaustion, brain fog and general achiness made it difficult for me to focus and to think straight. I felt that what had gone on in my mouth for so many years kept me from knowing — and being — the real me. These surgeries gave me the gift of coming face to face with who I really am, and what I am connected to — an infinite, unconditional, loving intelligence. I knew that I would never be the same again. Nor would I look at life in exactly the same way.

The dentist's assistant interrupted my musings and said something to me. She then gently removed the dark glasses from my face. I opened my eyes and looked over at my dentist, who looked back at me with a compassionate smile. The surgery was complete.

Chapter 22

I have been made happy by discovering that I have only added to the observations of other physicians, in pointing out a connection between the extraction of decayed and diseased teeth and the cure of general diseases.

Benjamin Rush, 1809

My dentist sent the tissue that he had removed during my dental revision to Dental DNA, a laboratory that tests for ninety pathogenic and virulent microbes. Dental DNA is unique in that they are able to identify bacteria, dead or alive, that were present at the time of the original root canal procedures, because the DNA is still present. Many of these bacteria can cause disease and are not normally found in a healthy mouth.

The body is host to many different kinds of bacteria. Its trillions of microorganisms outnumber the body's own cells ten to one! Bacteria start to colonize in the mouth soon after birth, forming communities called biofilms. These biofilms serve to prevent "pathogenic colonization" and train the immune system. In general, these beneficial bacteria help to keep the body's systems, such as the hormonal and nervous system, in good condition. The bacteria support good health and produce nutrients, and they play a critical role in determining our lifespan. These colonies of symbiotic bacteria work in tandem with our own body to influence our food choices, metabolism, behavior, mood and emotions. Without them, we could not survive. But bacteria can change from helpful to harmful; they can cause tooth decay (caries), abscesses and infectious disease.

There are three types of bacteria to consider here: aerobic bacteria, which can survive in oxygen-rich environments, anaerobic bacteria that live without oxygen and facultative bacteria that can adapt to either type of environment.

My Dental DNA report (Appendix B) listed twelve types of bacteria in my two root canals. Two were anaerobic and eight were facultative anaerobes. It is important to note that the anaerobic bacteria, the ones that survive without oxygen, become pathogenic in dead or damaged tissue, when trauma or surgery diminishes the blood supply. For this reason, a root canal, i.e. a dead tooth that no longer has nerves, a blood supply or a lymphatic system, is a perfect home to these toxic microbes.

Listed in the Dental DNA report were seven kinds of bacteria that are common to the mouth. Three types of streptococci (facultative anaerobic) were present. Strains of streptococci can cause infection after trauma caused either by injury or dental surgery. Streptococci can cause sepsis (blood poisoning), meningitis (inflammation of the membranes surrounding the brain and spinal cord) and pneumonia. Our immune system is not resistant to these harmful types of bacteria, which is an even bigger problem for those who are immune compromised. This may be why, according to Dr. Hal Huggins, these streptococci can do so much damage to the body.[27]

- Streptococcus gordonii causes bacterial endocarditis. In the bloodstream it colonizes platelet-fibrin thrombi, which can then colonize damaged heart valves.
- Streptococcus intermedius has a tendency to cause abscess formation, most commonly in the liver and brain. It can also affect the heart and nervous system.
- Streptococcus mutans creates cavities in teeth. It has been implicated in certain cardiovascular diseases, such as damaged and destroyed heart valve tissues and waxy plaque(s).

Besides streptococci as a potential cause of my bouts of pneumonia, I had three other contenders. This explained why I had been so susceptible to pneumonia and other respiratory infections. It all made sense.

- Pseudomonas aeruginosa, a facultative anaerobe, typically infects the lungs and urinary tract, along with burns and wounds, and can also cause blood infections.
- Stenotrophomonas maltophilia is an uncommon, tenacious and aerobic bacterium, making its infections hard to treat. It is a growing source of latent lung infections.
- Acinetobacter baumannii, an aerobic bacterium, is responsible for 80% of reported infections. These can range from pneumonia to serious blood or wound infections. They most commonly occur in ill patients, and can either cause or contribute to death.

Even though both Stenotrophomonas maltophilia and Acinetobacter baumannii are bacteria that must have an oxygenated environment in which to live, the report confirmed that these bacteria were present in the dental tubules at the time of the root canal procedure. I was dismayed to see these two strains of bacteria present in my DNA report. These bacteria found me an easy target since I had a compromised immune system. No wonder I had bacterial pneumonia several times a year. Under the circumstances, I feel lucky to have survived.

From my report, I understood that these different kinds of bacteria could affect specific organs in the body. I made a chart listing the parts of the body that each of these bacteria can affect. This exercise helped me to better understand what a focal infection is — an infection that originates in one part of the body, in this case the mouth, and affects another part of the body.

Lungs and Respiratory system: Acinetobacter baumannii, Actinomyces gerencseriae (previously known as Actinomyces israelii), Pseudomonas aeruginosa

Mouth: Acinetobacter baumannii, Actinomyces israelii, Porphyromonas endodontalis, Streptococcus gordonii, Streptococcus intermedius, Streptococcus mutans, Tannerella forsythensis

Gastrointestinal tract: Actinomyces gerencseriae (aka Actinomyces israelii)

Heart: Propionibacterium acnes, Pseudomonas aeruginosa, Stenotrophomonas maltophilia, Streptococcus gordonii, Streptococcus mutans

Urinary tract: Pseudomonas aeruginosa

Eyes: Propionibacterium acnes

Brain: Streptococcus intermedius

Liver and Spleen: Actinomyces israelii, Salmonella typhi, Streptococcus intermedius

Gall bladder: Salmonella typhi

Nervous system: Salmonella typhi, Acinetobacter baumannii, Pseudomonas aeruginosa

The pioneering dental-research specialist Dr. Weston Price found that people with a family history of disease often experienced the following illnesses after having root canals: migraines, sinusitis, colitis, thyroid disease, breast tumors, gallbladder disease, cystitis, eczema, heart valve issues, hypertension, coronary artery disease, iritis, pernicious anemia, neuritis and atherosclerosis.[28]

For twenty-five years, Dr. Weston Price carried out many root canal studies. These studies began with the support of the American Dental Association and were undertaken by its affiliated research institute.[29] Dr. Price took extracted root canals from sick patients and implanted them under the skin of rabbits, because they have immune systems similar to those of humans. When Dr. Price inserted an extracted root canal treated tooth from a patient who had suffered a heart attack, the rabbit would have a heart attack and die. Whatever illness or disease the patient had, when their tooth was embedded underneath the rabbit's skin, the rabbit almost always came down with the disease or illness of the patient![30]

Sterile objects such as coins were placed under the rabbits' skin. A sterile cyst-like covering would form, and there would be little change in the rabbits' health. When disease-free teeth were extracted for orthodontic reasons and embedded under the rabbits' skin, there were no reactions, even if the tooth was left there for a long period of time.

Dr. Price found that many diseases were transferred to the rabbits from the bacteria in the extracted teeth. This included heart and circulatory disease, joint issues such as arthritis and rheumatism, diseases of the brain and nervous system as well as kidney and bladder diseases, lung problems, mental disorders, pregnancy complications and many various degenerative diseases. Dr. Price discovered that different bacteria affect specific parts of the body.[31]

In his important research on focal infections, Dr. Charles Rosenow had also discovered that very fact, which he called the principle of "elective localization." Dr. Frank Billings found that 90% of focal infections originated from the tonsils and teeth. The concept of the mouth serving as a focal infection was not new. Hippocrates wrote in 400 BC that a patient's arthritis had been cured after a tooth extraction.[32] Furthermore, when Dr. Price extracted teeth that had had root canal procedures, many of these patients recovered from their illnesses!

Dr. Price's research, and that of his team of sixty scientists and doctors, was published in two volumes in 1923: *Dental Infections, Oral and Systemic* and volume two, *Dental Infections and the Degenerative Diseases.* By 1930, the concept of focal infection was controversial and had fallen out of favor. Dr. Price and his research, as well as that done by other doctors, were discredited and dismissed by the dental authorities.

Dr. Price's research was buried for almost seventy years, until Dr. George E. Meinig, a well-respected endodontist (root canal specialist) rediscovered Dr. Price's work. Dr. Meinig wrote in his own book, entitled *Root Canal Cover-Up*, that one of the most important discoveries of Dr. Price's research was that anaerobic bacteria in teeth with root canals act similarly to cancer cells in that they metastasize to other parts of the body.[33]

Dr. Price's remarkable work is still rejected by mainstream dental authorities today. However, by the 1980s, articles began to appear that associated gum disease with certain systemic conditions such as pneumonia and cardiovascular disease. With advancements in microbiology to identify microorganisms, previously unclassified organisms in the mouth had been discovered. It became obvious that "the oral cavity does indeed act as a reservoir of bacteria that metastasize to distant regions and cause disease in susceptible individuals."[34] "Periodontal medicine" was coined in 1996 to explain the relationship between periodontitis and systemic disease. While there is still much controversy surrounding the mouth and focal infections, there is consensus that more research is needed.

Dr. Hal Huggins, D.D.S., the founder of Dental DNA Laboratory, partnered with cardiologist Dr. Thomas Levy, M.D. in 1994 – 2000 to replicate Dr. Weston Price's research with advanced testing techniques. Their findings supported Dr. Price's research.[35] Toxins from anaerobic bacteria greatly affect the body's enzymes and immune system. These toxins kill enzymes that are vital for life, and create neurological, hormonal and autoimmune diseases and even mental illness.[36]

Dr. Boyd Haley, a scientist who tested root canal-treated teeth against brain enzymes, found that the toxins from the teeth had killed some or all of the enzymes needed for brain function. The teeth were always toxic; some more so than others. He commented in his foreword to *The Toxic Tooth*, that bacteria from the mouth "are basically the primary source of bacteria that causes most systemic infection."[37]

Modern-day technology confirms Dr. Weston Price's theory of focal infection.[38] Thanks to Polymerase Chain Reaction (PCR), considered the most important scientific advancement in microbiology, segments of DNA can actually be amplified and copied. According to Dr. Haley, many PCR studies have identified pathogenic bacteria in organs of patients that were also found in their root canal-treated teeth.[39]

Chapter 23

The goal of life is to make your heartbeat match the beat of the universe, to match your nature with Nature.

Joseph Campbell

As each day passed, I felt better and better. I was excited by all the little changes. I no longer had a chronically stuffy nose. My sense of smell continued to improve. The big surprise was that my sense of taste (which I did not realize was not up to par) was enhanced as well. The subtle flavors of the organic, whole foods I ate were now like a symphony of tastes bursting forth in my mouth! I also started digesting my food better. I slept more soundly at night and felt more rested during the day. I was no longer stiff from sitting or lying down. In my exercise classes, to my amazement, I noticed that I had greater flexibility. Overall, I felt more relaxed and grounded.

To build up my stamina for my last surgery, I decided to walk the Wiggs twice a day for an hour each time. We went in the morning before breakfast and we walked again in the evening. The early morning hours were quiet and cool. The looming red rocks and the national forest bordered the empty streets in the adjoining neighborhoods that we passed through. I usually let Wiggles lead the way. I was always curious to see where he would take us. One morning I decided to walk earlier than usual. The sun slowly rose, and the ground was still damp with dew from the brief rain that had quenched the ground at daybreak. I enjoyed the smell of the fresh, clean air. There was almost a slight chill as Wiggles and I made our way up and down the streets.

This particular morning, the Wiggs took me down a horseshoe-shaped street that had outlets on either end. As we strolled over to the far side of the road, I felt my body slightly stiffen. As I became more alert, I had the overriding sense that everything would be fine. Besides, I wanted to see the progress that had been made on the one-story stucco house on the corner, which was vacant and being remodeled. As we approached the house, Wiggles hung back a little. I took a few more steps until I was at the end of the cement driveway. I glanced at Wiggs, whose tail was now down, with his gaze intently fixed on the garage. When I turned around, a large, dark-brown dog charged down the driveway, growling and baring his sharp, long teeth. I had never seen this vicious dog before. I noticed that fastened around his neck was a red collar and a clumsily tied rope that trailed behind him. He obviously had gotten free. I had neither pepper spray nor anything else with which to defend myself. But for some unknown reason I had no fear. I felt oddly self-confident, and did not feel I was in any danger. My body did not go into fight-or-flight mode. I felt grounded as my body took over. I became the observer.

Everything moved in slow motion now. A pleasant rhythm hummed through my body and mind. It felt matter-of-fact, yet special at the same time. In that moment, I could not differentiate myself from the large dog, Wiggs or the surrounding houses, streets, trees, or even the canyon beyond. I was keenly aware that I was part of a larger whole, one with something that everything possessed. I had never been so fully engaged in the moment or felt so alive. As I watched the dog get closer, his mouth wide open, I could have sworn my feet had grown roots down through the asphalt and into the rocky red soil underneath. Spontaneously, I took a very deep deliberate breath, tilted my head back and opened my mouth. Out of my throat came a loud, high-pitched, primordial squeal that cut through the morning air. The peculiar sound vibrated through every cell in my body and made me feel as if I had just put my finger in an electric socket.

The big dog stopped in its tracks and grew quiet. Before I could do anything else, the ground started to vibrate. Not sure about what was happening, the dog looked at me. I stared back at the dog. From around the corner came four large javelinas, stampeding toward us. Javelinas look like wild boars with short and coarse salt-and-pepper colored hair, short legs and a pig-like snout. Long, sharp canine teeth protrude from their jaws about an inch, which make them look fierce and scary. I felt a sense of wonder as the javelinas neared. Wiggles moved quickly and now stood trembling between my legs. The attack dog turned and wasted no time as he made a beeline up the driveway and out of sight. I stood perfectly still and held my breath. If I had reached out my hand, I could have touched the javelinas as they moved quickly past me, kicking up dirt and dust, which made me sneeze and cough. They were gone as fast as they appeared. I picked up Wiggles and ran all the way home.

That night as I told my husband about my experience, it occurred to me that I had called the javelinas to come to my rescue. It was as if a part of me knew that they were nearby and that the Wiggs and I would be fine. The whole experience was magical. I pondered that energy of connection I had so plainly felt. I thought back to the near-death experience that I'd had years earlier, when I first moved to Arizona. I recalled experiencing this same energy, which I was a part of, and which connected me to everything else. It felt neither positive nor negative; but it softly and smoothly pulsated and enlivened everything. I have always wondered about the nature of that energy; what was it exactly? At that moment I knew. I began to tell my husband about an experience I'd had years ago after my mom died.

Leading up to my mom's diagnosis of cancer, she had struggled with chronic fatigue syndrome and fibromyalgia, along with the arthritis she'd had for most of her adult life. After her untimely death, my sister and I cleaned out her house to get it ready to sell. I sat at her desk and opened its drawers for the last time, just as I had when I was a child. There was an array of papers and old receipts. It was the "everything drawer," where my mom placed the things that were unimportant but not ready to throw out yet. I had started to gather them up when I felt compelled to stop and carefully look through her papers of old receipts, to-do notes, recipes and shopping lists.

There was nothing remarkable until I got to a sheet from her meditation class. She began to meditate again after her diagnosis of chronic fatigue syndrome. Across the top of the paper, she had written the question: "Why does my body hurt so much?" She went on to write about the experience she'd had during her meditation. On the bottom of the page she had written in large, capital letters,

"LOVE IS THE ANSWER."

I sat back in my chair, somewhat disappointed. It did not make sense; it did not seem to answer her question. I could almost see the look of puzzlement and frustration on my mom's face.

Love is the answer. My mom's meditation from all those years ago has continued to linger in my mind. It is a stock phrase that is so overused that it has become somewhat meaningless. After my experience with the dog and the javelinas that morning, I realized that my mom *did* get the answer to her question. Love *is* the answer. It occurred to me that love is not a fleeting emotion; it is the state of being. It is the energy of which everything is made — nature, ourselves, our thoughts and words and the life we create. What I had learned during my near-death experience now made sense: There is no "negative energy;" there is only love. What is called bad or negative energy does not exist, it is in fact just a turning-away from or a form of resistance to love.

My adventure with the Wiggs helped me to remember our connection to love that always is. I thought back to my second surgery. I realized that it was this energy — the energy of love — that I had experienced. Love is the answer. I could choose to live my life by being mindful that love is at the root of everything, because that is the fact — whether I acknowledge it or not. By simply embracing loving thoughts and actions and allowing love to flow and speak through me, everything, somehow, would work out. The decisions and correct choices would become obvious. The people, places and things that I would need in order to live a life full of love, abundance and happiness would show up at the perfect time. What happened to me, day in and day out, was no longer the point: the point was how I chose to respond! I could choose love, or I could choose to resist that all-encompassing energy. That piece of paper, long forgotten by my mom in her drawer, was a gift to me. I smiled and thought of Princess Bia and the half-opened drawer in her box. It took finding my mom's meditation in *her* desk to uncover the mystery of what message the Princess's drawer had held for me.

In a few short weeks I would undergo my last dental surgery. Through my newfound stamina, strength, confidence and clarity, I now knew how to prepare myself. Above all, I needed to be the love that I am, to honor it, and to allow that energy of love to be my guide. Through mindfulness and releasing any and all resistance, I could draw upon the wisdom of my heart and access my deep well of inner resources. A part of me already knew what needed to be done. My body also had far greater wisdom and knowledge of how to heal itself than I did.

Yes, Mom — love *is* always the answer!

Chapter 24

Facts are stubborn things; and whatever may be our wishes, our inclinations, or the dictates of our passion, they cannot alter the state of facts and evidence.

John Adams

I looked up and smiled at my biological dentist. Mindfully, I looked around the small, airy room and let out a big sigh as my shoulders relaxed. I gently touched the heart pendant that hung around my neck, which had become my talisman, silently repeating the inscription on the reverse side — "Boldly go into the great and vast unknown" — while I nestled back against the comfortable reclining chair. I closed my eyes as his assistant placed the dark glasses on my face once again. The cuff on my forearm tightened as I listened to the beeping of the machine that took my blood pressure.

I felt better prepared for this third surgery than the first two because now I knew what to expect. Even so, each surgery had been a very different experience. For this surgery, I felt greater vitality, and I felt physically and mentally stronger than ever before. Many of the symptoms I had lived with for years had disappeared. I could not wait to see what would happen next.

After I'd been prepped, it was finally time to begin. My biological dentist would clean out the last two cavitations, where the bone had died due to lack of blood supply and not being properly cleaned out in the first place. These were on the left side of my mouth, at the sites where the upper and lower wisdom teeth had been extracted when I was twenty.

I drifted in and out as I heard the voices of my dentist and his assistant as they worked diligently and expertly to clean out the two cavitations. What they found is so commonplace that it did not surprise them, but it did me. As the surgery progressed and the thin, boney caps were removed, two large holes emerged where my wisdom teeth had been. Encircled by a ring of crystallized, calcified bone, the jawbone around and in the extraction site had harbored infection and inflammation in the bone marrow, called "osteomyelitis." My biological dentist had told me that an infected tooth is usually accompanied by bacterial infection, both in the periodontal ligament and in the tooth's socket. Mine was no different.

But this is not what surprised me. What astonished me was that both holes had become receptacles for mercury! I'd had mercury fillings when I was a kid, but those fillings were removed in my mid-thirties. The only thing that I could figure was that during those years after I had my wisdom teeth extracted, and before I had the mercury fillings removed, the metal particles from the amalgams had migrated into the empty holes in the jawbone! Years ago, a dentist had told me that mercury fillings are stable in the mouth and do not break down. Based on my experience, I now believe that mercury-amalgam fillings are not stable.

I thought back to the woman I had met when I lived in Washington, D.C., when I was in my thirties. She told me how she had helped her body become healthier by having her mercury fillings removed. Several years earlier, she had seen an episode of the TV show, *60 Minutes,* about amalgam fillings used in cavities.[40] Amalgam means mixed with mercury. From the show, she learned that her silver fillings contained fifty percent mercury or more, and that mercury can be even more poisonous than lead or arsenic. She said that silver fillings were never tested for safety, and that there is no safe threshold for mercury. Moreover, mercury vapor is released when you chew gum, eat food or grind your teeth at night.

60 Minutes interviewed people with health problems such as arthritis and multiple sclerosis (MS). MS is a disease that affects the brain, spinal cord and optic nerves. It creates problems with vision, muscle control, balance and other body functions. The people interviewed had decided to have their mercury fillings removed. Many of their health issues disappeared immediately after the surgery.

My new friend told me that after the surgery, her headaches, brain fog and depression cleared up. She then told me that she went to a naturopathic doctor who helped guide her on a detox protocol to remove the residual mercury from her body. After her detox, all of her MS symptoms were gone and have never returned. I would later learn that mercury can cause many different kinds of symptoms, based on a person's genetic weaknesses and general state of health. Autoimmune diseases such as my friend's MS, she deduced, had resulted from her exposure to mercury in her fillings, which could have triggered her genetic disposition to this disease.[41]

After speaking with her, I gave a lot of thought about the mercury in my mouth. I called my mainstream dentist, who assured me that the fillings posed no health risks and that the composition of the fillings (mercury mixed with silver, copper, tin and zinc) was stable. When pressed, he did concede that a very low dose of vapor was released when chewing, but that this was no cause for concern.

While I was on the phone, I thought about the proximity of my mouth to my brain. I wondered where the vapor from my fillings went. I would later learn that mercury vapor is inhaled into the lungs and travels throughout the bloodstream to every part of the body, including the brain. Mercury vapor is perhaps the deadliest form of mercury.[42] The Environmental Protection Agency had declared amalgams a hazardous substance in 1989.[43] If mercury was hazardous for the environment, then I did not want it in my body's environment. I felt strongly that I wanted to have my mercury fillings removed.

I found a dentist in the area who was able to remove them safely, by using a rubber dam placed in my mouth to protect me from swallowing any of the mercury. I also wore an oxygen mask so that I would not breathe in the vapors. For the next year, I used a detox protocol to remove the residual mercury that had, over time, traveled from my mouth to other areas of my body. I believed that the amalgams in my mouth were not stable — even though the dental community insisted amalgams are stable and chemically inactive, while admitting that chewing released mercury vapor.[44]

I recalled the good results I'd had after my mercury fillings were removed. I thought of the metallic taste I'd had in my mouth since childhood, which disappeared when my mercury fillings were gone. Food then tasted different, and even better. My bleeding and slightly inflamed gums healed; my cold hands and feet became noticeably warmer. I no longer had dizzy spells. I also noticed that the dark cloud of melancholy that sometimes followed me was gone. Though removing the mercury improved my overall health, it did not get rid of all my symptoms. For that, I would have to wait another twenty years to find my biological dentist.

I was so excited by the results from the removal of my amalgam fillings, that I could not wait to share the news with family and friends. Many of them listened cautiously to what I had achieved. Some were aware of the controversy surrounding mercury amalgams. They responded mostly with confusion and disbelief. Their dentists had told them that amalgams were perfectly safe. Amalgams had been used for a long time, and the American Dental Association approved them.

I felt as if they had not heard what I had just shared with them. I naively repeated my results and waited for it to compute, but they seemed to discount my experience. I began to understand that they had no point of reference; they had never even thought about their mouth having any correlation with their overall health.

I turned my attention back to the surgery to clean out my cavitations. As my biological dentist removed the mercury from the last cavitation, something wonderful began to occur. I felt clearheaded. The low-grade buzzing noise in my head was gone! My mind was peaceful and quiet — yes! For once! My dentist then sewed up the sites where the cavitations had been.

This time, I thought back to my college days and how I'd witnessed my vitality dry up. Feelings of shame, confusion and doubt surfaced and swooshed through me. My memory had become so bad over the years that I would be in the middle of a sentence and would totally lose my train of thought. I had felt so fuzzy and foggy. But now, thanks to this final cavitation surgery, I felt clearheaded! I could recall the facts in great detail from a book I had read the week before. My body relaxed further as I settled deeper into the chair, while my biological dentist finished his work.

I later asked my biological dentist if my results were similar to everyone else's. He told me that each person's experience is always different. Some people experience changes to their health immediately while others do not, and sometimes the improvements occur over time. Sometimes it seems as if nothing changes. This can mean that the patient needs to work further on their overall health with a qualified integrative, functional-medicine or naturopathic doctor. He reminded me that removing the toxic load in the mouth is often just one of many steps that must be taken to revitalize the body and enable it to fully heal. Everyone is different. I had already done a great deal of work over the years to support my body.

After this final surgery, I noticed that my entire body was so quiet. I realized that I had lived with a certain level of "noisiness" inside for much of my life. Living in my body now felt strangely peaceful and solid. It is hard to describe what I mean. All I can say is that I now experience a level of silence that feels peaceful, grounding and really good.

Over the next several weeks, I noticed that feelings and emotions flowed easily through me. They no longer got stuck, and no longer showed up as tightness and pain in my body. This is the art of letting go at its best. Happily, the tightness in my hips, shoulders and neck, and the last of my general aches and pains completely disappeared. I continued to watch in awe as my body healed and changed for the better.

Chapter 25

By weight you are more human than bacteria, because your cells are bigger, but by numbers, it's not even close.

Dr. Bonnie Bassler

With the completion of my last dental surgery, I felt deeply relieved. The answers to my health questions did indeed reside in my mouth. Every day, my vitality and overall health continued to improve. I finally had the energy to get things done. I was now on life's playing field instead of sitting on the sidelines. I not only noticed the world around me, but it was as if I were seeing it for the first time. I relished and found pleasure in my home — and in the looming majestic red rocks that created such a dynamic view — as I never had before. With the exhaustion gone, I looked forward to everything now. My spirit soared! The smallest task became fun as I flowed from experience to experience. I loved my newfound energy, vitality and creativity. I was animated and excited about my life and living. During my follow-up visit to remove the stitches, I told my biological dentist that I felt as if I were twenty again. It was as if my body had picked up where it had left off, before the extraction of my wisdom teeth.

I was anxious to get the last laboratory report from Dental DNA. (Appendix C)

My final report from Dental DNA listed many different types of bacteria found in my two cavitations. It continued to answer many of my health questions. Seventeen types of bacteria were present in one of the cavitations (tooth #16) and sixteen in the other cavitation (tooth #17)! I was not surprised to see the five types of toxic bacteria that caused respiratory illness, including pneumonia.

- Acinetobacter baumannii appeared for both teeth; this causes 80% of reported infections from a variety of illnesses, including pneumonia.

  Since this organism was found in my root canals as well, I could surmise that this was a common aerobic bacterium (which needs oxygen to live) in my body. This certainly was not a comforting thought!
- Haemophilus influenzae causes pneumonia
- Hafnia alvei can cause pneumonia in immune-compromised individuals,
- Corynebacterium diphtheriae is found in upper-respiratory illnesses
- Enterobacter cloacae creates lower-respiratory infections.

The list also included three kinds of anaerobic bacteria (which do not need oxygen to live) that cause urinary tract infections (UTI). I had started having frequent bouts of UTI in my early twenties after my wisdom teeth were extracted. They were an annoying and uncomfortable infection that I'd been dealing with, several times a year, for the past thirty years. These bacteria were:

- Enterobacter cloacae
- Enterococcus faecalis
- Prevotella melaninogenica

As I read over the report, I felt a profound sense of relief. Smiling, I nodded my head. The information contained in the dental report confirmed that my body and I had done nothing wrong all these years. I was excited to finally experience the level of energy, stamina and vitality that I had known when I was a teenager.

I now felt strongly based on my personal experience that bacteria and their toxic waste found in my cavitations and root canals *did* affect my immune system, and *did* cause a focal infection that resulted in symptoms. Again, I made a list of what organs are affected by these organisms:

<u>Lungs and Respiratory system</u>: Acinetobacter baumannii, Candida (which is a fungus), Corynebacterium diphtheriae, Enterobacter aerogenes, Streptococcus constellatus, Eikenella corrodens, Enterobacter cloacae, Hafnia alvei, Peptostreptococcus micros, Prevotella melaninogenica, Rothia dentocariosa

<u>Mouth</u>: Acinetobacter baumannii, Streptococcus intermedius, Streptococcus mutans, Veillonella parvula, Candida, Streptococcus constellatus, Streptococcus mitis, Eikenella corrodens, Peptostreptococcus micros, Prevotella melaninogenica, Rothia dentocariosa

<u>Gastrointestinal tract</u>: Bacillus cereus, Candida, Enterobacter aerogenes, Hafnia alvei, Peptostreptococcus micros

<u>Heart</u>: Stenotrophomonas maltophilia, Streptococcus gordonii, Streptococcus mutans, Candida, Corynebacterium

diphtheriae, Enterobacter aerogenes, Neisseria mucosa, Streptococcus constellatus, Streptococcus mitis, Enterobacter cloacae, Rothia dentocariosa

Urinary tract: Pseudomonas aeruginosa, Veillonella parvula, Candida, Enterobacter aerogenes, enterobacter cloacae, Hafnia alvei, peptostreptococcus micros, provettella melaninogenica, enterococcus faecalis

Eyes: Propionibacterium acnes, Candida, Enterobacter cloacae, Hafnia alvei

Brain: Streptococcus intermedius, Veillonella parvula, Candida, Streptococcus constellatus

Liver and Spleen: Actinomyces israelii, Salmonella typhi, Streptococcus intermedius, Candida, Streptococcus constellatus, Peptostreptococcus micros

Nervous system: Acinetobacter baumannii, Candida, Corynebacterium diphtheriae, Enterobacter aerogenes, Kingella oralis

Skeletal system: Haemophilus aphrophilus, Enterobacter cloacae, Hafnia alvei, Prevotella melaninogenica

Skin: Enterobacter cloacae, Peptostreptococcus micros

According to Dr. Hal Huggins, the founder of the lab, when the periodontal ligament is left behind after a tooth extraction and the jawbone is not properly scraped and cleaned to remove all infection, the formation of a "really good blood clot" is compromised. The blood clot is essential in the healing process and the growth of new bone.[45] Until the boney cap forms over the top of the extraction site, over seven hundred species of bacteria, as well as fungi, viruses, protozoa and mycoplasma that live in the mouth, have access to that area.[46] As the cap grows over the site, the socket becomes oxygen deprived as the damaged tissue dies from the lack of blood flow.

The trapped bacteria's genes mutate into more virulent forms, which enables the pathogenic bacteria to adapt to their new environment.[47] Furthermore, when pathogenic bacteria reach a certain mass, they can turn on genes that make them more virulent as well.[48]

The goal of all bacteria is simply to survive and reproduce. They do not want to intentionally harm the body and endanger their host. On the contrary, bacteria play an important role in human health; they contribute over eight million genes to our 23,000. The human body possesses three hundred and sixty times more bacterial genes than genes from our own cells![49] Healthy bacterial genes contribute to our health and well-being, and are our greatest ally. They allow our bodies to quickly adapt to changes, and they greatly add to our overall quality of life. However, bacterial genes that must mutate in order to survive in an unhealthy environment are harmful to our bodies.

Virulence factors allow bacteria to survive in these unhealthy environments. High mutation rates and a short lifespan enable pathogenic bacteria to pass along characteristics that make the next generation both more hardy and more virulent. The downside is that these factors cause disease, and make future generations of these bacteria difficult to kill. There are over two hundred and twenty known toxins from bacteria. It is the virulent toxins that cause our illness and disease, and not the bacteria themselves. Two of these poisonous substances produced by bacteria, mentioned in my lab reports from Dental DNA, were endotoxins and exotoxins.[50]

Endotoxins are toxic substances within the cell walls of bacteria, which are released when they rupture. They create havoc in the entire body, causing immune responses such as fever, inflammation, diarrhea and vomiting. Endotoxins can sometimes be lethal.

Exotoxins, secreted by bacteria or excreted at the time of bacterial cell death, are more specific in their actions. They destroy parts of human cells or inhibit metabolic functions. Exotoxins can be classified as:

1. Neurotoxins (poison that affects the nervous system)
2. Enterotoxins (poison that affects the intestines)
3. Cytotoxins (poisons that affect cells)

Exotoxins can travel from a “focus of infection” (such as the mouth) to other parts of the body and cause damage. For example, Pseudomonas aeruginosa, found in my two extracted root canals, create a toxin that can shut down liver function. (Personal communication, Dr. Robert Wheeler, Assistant Lab Director of Dental DNA Laboratories, October 6, 2015). This could be the reason why I experienced liver issues. Diphtheria toxin is also an exotoxin, secreted from the pathogenic bacterium Corynebacterium diphtheriae. This toxin creates inflammation in the throat, which obstructs swallowing and breathing. It also damages the heart and nerves, which can cause death. Another example is the botulinum neurotoxin, secreted by the pathogenic bacterium Clostridium botulinum, which is considered the most toxic substance ever identified; only one milligram would be needed to kill a million guinea pigs![51]

Dr. Boyd Haley found that many of the toxins produced by pathogenic bacteria from cavitations and some root canals were a hundred to a thousand times more deadly than botulism — some of the deadliest he had ever encountered. He told Dr. Huggins that whatever these toxins were, they certainly did not belong in the mouth.[52] Dr. Haley called these toxins "small-molecule toxicants" and discovered that they were much more toxic than either endotoxins or exotoxins. He found that small-molecule toxicants, "besides being enzyme inhibitors, are not interfered with by antibodies of the immune system, and these toxicants also kill immune-system cells." Many of these toxicants have yet to be identified; more research is needed. (Personal communication, Dr. Boyd Haley, March 1, 2016).

Looking at my lab reports, I came to the conclusion that the bacteria listed there had affected the overall function of my body. I felt the bacteria's virulent factors and toxic waste had kept my immune system on high alert, and perhaps even disabled it. These endotoxins, exotoxins and small-molecule toxicants seemed to create an inner distress that I could never escape from. Now that the fountain of toxins had been turned off, my immune system could recover and my body could finally heal.

As I read through my lab reports, I realized how lucky I was to have access to this information, as well as access to a biological dental professional who had initiated profound changes in both my health and the quality of my life. As I worked diligently to resolve my health issues for the past thirty years, I came to the conclusion that something had kept my body from healing itself. I believed that in order to enhance its survival, the body has a reason for everything it does. I felt that I was in partnership with my body and symptoms were a way for my body to communicate. I responded by creating a new and improved environment to support greater health and vitality. This meant going through a dental revision to remove any toxicity. This also entailed changes in diet and lifestyle, supplementing with vitamins, minerals, herbs and finding better ways to manage stress.

Chapter 26

Two roads diverged in a wood and I — I took the one less traveled by, and that has made all the difference.

Robert Frost

My dental revision has breathed new life into my body. I can now focus for long periods of time, and my memory has improved. I have more energy and stamina, I require less sleep, and I no longer need to take naps! I find that I now dream in brilliant colors.[53] My digestion and elimination have also greatly improved, and I am no longer plagued by any of the symptoms that had been identified as chronic fatigue syndrome or Epstein-Barr virus. My immune system is strong and robust. Overall, I have witnessed the healing power of my body — now that a tremendous amount of stress from my mouth, in the form of toxicity from my dental work — has been removed. It is amazing that after thirty years of what turned out to be the management of unresponsive symptoms, my dental revision resolved most of my health issues. But there is still work to be done. (Fig. 8)

Effect of Dental Revisions on Symptoms
Symptoms Resolved After First Surgery (cavitations, right side)
• Low energy, exhaustion • Arthritis in right hand • Low blood pressure • Swollen lymph nodes in neck • Brain fog, memory loss • Unable to sleep through the night, unrefreshing sleep
Symptoms Resolved After Second Surgery (root canals removed)
• Dehydration • Hypothyroidism • Low cortisol levels • Unable to smell, stuffy nose • Sense of taste • Hypoglycemia
Symptoms Resolved After Third Surgery (cavitations, left side)
• Lack of well-being, blocked creativity • Urinary tract infections • Indigestion, gas, bloating, constipation • Panic attacks • Bad breath • Prone to illness, difficulty recovering • Chronic Fatigue Syndrome, Epstein-Barr
Symptoms Resolved Within Two Years After Surgeries
• Respiratory infections, bacterial pneumonia • Astigmatism, right eye • Frequent plantar warts • Unhealthy skin, hair and nails • Skin rashes, hives, muscle pain, stiffness, swelling • Heavy-metal load of copper and mercury
Symptoms That Have Improved
• Hormonal imbalance • Liver issues • Adrenal Fatigue

Fig. 8 Symptoms

After a dental revision, the body needs support. Dr. Hal Huggins mentions in his book, *Uninformed Consent*, that the body can now detoxify itself more efficiently and effectively once the fountain — or in my case, the geyser of toxins is turned off. Care must be taken to make sure the body is able to get rid of the waste as quickly as it is released. If not, the waste will just be redistributed, and could result in sickness.[54] Diet, a healthy lifestyle, supplementation of nutrients; hydration, appropriate natural therapies, gentle exercise and rest all were imperative to the overall success of my healing process during the two years after my dental revision.

Over the ensuing weeks after my final surgery, my mind became quicker and my creativity began to flow more easily. I was inspired to invent creative solutions that nurtured and nourished me, and met my needs in solving everyday problems. I began to fill notebooks with different ideas and portions of paragraphs that would lead me to realize my childhood dream of becoming a writer — a dream that I had abandoned in college after my wisdom teeth were removed.

After my final cavitation surgery, I dreamt that I was sitting at a table, typing away on my laptop. A gentleman walked over to me and handed me two large plastic bags filled with fish heads. I looked approvingly at the fish heads, as I marveled how bright and clear the eyes were — a sign of freshness and good health! In dream interpretation, fish heads represent the unused portion of potential. I was now given the opportunity to use that underutilized part of my own potential — my creativity! I realized that my potential, the ability to fully experience and grow from life's experiences, had never really left me. If anything, one of the gifts from my health challenges was to learn, grow and mature.

I began to look at every experience I went through as a catalyst for positive change. There was a gift in everything that happened, and I would find it if I did not judge, label or criticize. It was there somewhere. Through self-acceptance and self-awareness, I recognized the potential transition from relying solely on institutions and authority figures to the wisdom and clarity that reside within my own heart, soul and body. I had become my own authority.

I have learned that the body has several resources for communication. While symptoms represent one way, emotions and feelings provide another and very different avenue for the body to speak. Emotions ask simple questions that need to be answered in a thoughtful and honest manner. The insight afforded by my emotions allowed me to turn my attention inwards, and patiently await the inspired action that would eventually emerge. I learned how to tune into my body's needs at any given moment. I asked questions with the intention and belief that they would be answered. More importantly, through wisdom, I learned what questions were worth asking and what questions would actually get to the root cause of the issue. Often I was surprised by the answers.

My thirty years of exhaustion is gone. I realized how differently I had perceived both my life and the world around me. Being sick most of the time, and being tired all of the time, had created a blurry lens through which I had been forced to view my life. The best example I can give of how I had experienced my life was like eating very bland, lukewarm mashed potatoes covered in tasteless lumpy gravy on a white plate. Life looked and felt flat, muted, dull and colorless. It took great effort to see anything else, because I lived under an umbrella of exhaustion, brain fog and an assortment of aches and pains. I did not know how much different life could be, because I had nothing to compare with my daily experiences.

But my dental revision changed all of that. Life is now like piping-hot mashed potatoes that taste mild and earthy, with a bright flavor, served on a brilliant lapis-blue plate. The slightly salty dark-brown gravy, in contrast, lends a roasted, robust flavor. Its silky texture complements the light, fluffy mashed potatoes. Life is alive! My senses are keener; colors are more vibrant; I am more mindful of my environment. Everything has a scent that I can actually smell. Food tastes better. I have a better feel and sense of the textures, patterns and overall structure of the world around me. The world is energized, and it hums and vibrates. I feel connected to and a part of everything. I am no longer isolated and lonely. I have the energy to respond to life, to smile, to laugh and to see the world empathetically, from many perspectives.

I continue to develop an even greater and more joyful awareness, and to respond in even more creative and productive ways. I have learned to let go of what I think I need, and what I think must change, for me to be happy. On my journey of the past thirty years, I have never blamed anyone or anything for the problems and sorrows in my life. I have always looked straight in the mirror and realized that I can change nothing but myself. I now choose to love myself, and to say yes to the best that life has to offer. YES! I strive to serve my health and myself in productive, constructive and loving ways. My life is no longer stagnant. Magic and joy flow more steadily into my daily experiences. I look forward to every day, and I delight in the perfect people, places and things I need — which show up magically at the perfect moment.

When I first arrived in Sedona, a gentleman told me that this town brings out the best in people. Often people's best is hidden under a lot of other stuff, but eventually Sedona has her way. Life has a funny way of providing what is most needed. I had always wondered why I was here in Sedona.

Recently, I met with the health consultant who had placed me on the path to resolve my health issues through biological dentistry. My body is in flux. I have improved my liver health. My adrenal fatigue is resolving. Now that my body can properly detox, and has the time to do so, my latest hair mineral analysis showed that my heavy-metal load of mercury and copper is gone! I did not have to do anything to accomplish this amazing feat but continue with my healthy lifestyle.

As I stood up to leave from my appointment, I paused. My health consultant looked at me as she opened the door, and wistfully said, in her German accent, "You know, it is a good thing that you came here to Sedona." I smiled and felt thankful. The move to Sedona, and my health challenges, had not taken me off my life's path as I had imagined. It had actually put me *on* my path, entrusting me to take the next steps towards a brand-new period of purpose, meaning and joy.

Chapter 27

Love conquers all.

Virgil

Healing is a matter of time, but it is also sometimes a matter of opportunity.

Hippocrates

I find myself at an interesting crossroads, a crossroads where the majority of my time has been freed up from spending so much of it taking care of my health. In the aftermath of my surgeries, there is still some work to be done — but this time there is a different sense of urgency, one in which I see a light at the end of a long tunnel. It is satisfying to watch as my body works to heal and fine-tune itself. I now find that I do not need to take many supplements, or do therapies, or sleep as much as I did before.

My work has changed — instead of just trying to figure out how to make it through the day, I can spend my time fully enjoying the here and now. I have a future worth dreaming about, how I want to feel and look in my body, where I want to go and what I want to do. It is a very different paradigm from looking at myself as sick, focused only on what I wanted to change.

The question I would ask myself was "Who *would* I be if I did not have to focus on getting well all the time?" Since my dental revisions, my identity has shifted, and it is time to think of myself in a whole new way. The question quickly became "Who *will* I be, now that I have my health back?" I cannot recapture the past thirty years, and I really would not want to. I am who I am because of my trials and tribulations, my victories and losses.

On reflection upon my lifelong pursuit to reclaim my health, I ended up discovering what makes for a happy and healthy life. I think one of the main ingredients is paradoxical: never be satisfied. For me, life's challenges became opportunities for greater clarity. New decisions and choices ultimately led to greater satisfaction and adventure. Life is an opportunity to ask increasingly interesting questions, and to enjoy the ways in which the answers effortlessly present themselves.

One of the biggest gifts from my dental revision has been the return of my energy. This has translated into a keen interest and curiosity, tinged with excitement and exhilaration, about the world around me. There is so much to experience, learn and share. Each and every day, I wake up well rested and count my blessings. It is AMAZING to wake up and feel great! I feel like a teenager again! Sometimes I literally want to run up to the top of the red rocks and scream, "I'm here! I'm ready! I'm alive!"

I have carried with me the passionate knowing that my body could and would heal. I have experienced and learned more about dentistry and health through my need to get healthy and support my body in its process. I have not only learned about the connection between my mouth and my health, but also about the importance of my connection to myself. The mouth is the entrance, the gate to an inner world that connects the physical body to the mind and ultimately to the soul. The Hindu story of Krishna (the embodiment of love and divine joy) is one of my favorite illustrations of this point.

As a child, Krishna greatly enjoyed playing outdoors in the mud. As children often do, he would place his muddy hands in his mouth. His mother Yashoda became upset. She asked little Krishna to open his mouth wide, so she could look inside to see how much mud he had eaten. As she leaned forward, a miraculous sight engulfed her. Within her child's mouth she saw the entire universe, gleaming with brightly lit stars! She saw the sun and moon, planet Earth with its continents and oceans, and even their hometown! Astonished as she was, she leaned into her son's mouth for a closer look: and there she saw herself, looking into Krishna's mouth.

While our own mouths do not seem to harbor such miraculous views, they in fact do. The mouth embodies our own inner universe, teeming with life and possibilities. What is placed into the mouth — the gateway to the body — directly affects our health: how we feel, how we look, how we behave, how we think, as well as our overall well-being. It can support or hinder us in our ability to be our authentic selves. The connection between diet and health is well accepted. We know that a healthy diet creates a strong, vital and resilient body. But dentistry is a different story. I believe that extraction sites, root canals and the dental materials used in teeth can quickly eclipse the expression of the magnificence we all possess. The fact that after my dental revision, my symptoms disappeared and I regained my health, vitality and creativity, is proof enough for me that in my case, there was a direct cause-and-effect link.

After my first dental surgery, I went for a checkup with my physician. I had promised him that I would stay on top of the swollen lymph nodes in my neck. I could not wait for him to see that the lumps were totally gone, and my lymph was back to normal. During my appointment, he felt my neck carefully for signs of the swollen lymph glands. A big smile spread over his face as he realized there were no longer any lumps. I could hardly contain myself as I excitedly told him about my biological dentist, my cavitations and the petroleum medicament that could never be broken down. I explained that when my biological dentist opened the site, it spewed and bubbled with infection. I then told my doctor that when the socket was cleaned out, my lymph let go! My doctor did not say anything. He looked at me with interest as his eyes shared my relief and happiness. I felt triumphant.

That night I dreamt that I sat on the examination table in my doctor's office. He came in with a tongue depressor in his hand and asked me to open my mouth wide. He gasped as he quickly picked up a mirror to show me the view. Within my mouth, I saw a swirl of colors: gold, orange, green, pink, blue and purple. Stars shone bright, which at a closer look were replicas of my pendant. They cast their light on a field of lupines — the tall, colorful spires of blossoms with brilliant bluish-purple, purple and pink flower spikes and kelly green, palm-shaped leaves found in my daughters' book, *Miss Rumphius*. My doctor turned toward me as he placed the mirror on the table and asked, "What will you do now to make the world more beautiful?"

The dream left an indelible impression upon me. I look forward to answering this question every day for the rest of my life.

Chapter 28

For last year's words belong to last year's language
And next year's words await another voice.
And to make an end is to make a beginning.

T.S. Eliot

The summer after my final surgery, I went on a vacation with my husband and Mr. Wiggles to visit my family in Maine. In the past, traveling and even day trips were things I was very hesitant and afraid to do, since I never knew how I would feel. With my challenged immune system, I was susceptible to catching colds, flus and viruses. Once I got ill, it was difficult for me to recover. But after my dental revision was complete, I looked forward to traveling and had no fears about my health.

We spent much of our trip out on the hiking trails, which were covered in soft layers of dried-out, brown-colored pine needles in the cool, crisp, fragrance-filled air. We enjoyed the beautiful scenery of baby-blue skies, dark-green pine trees, pink-and-gray granite rocks covered with blue-green moss, mountains, crystal-clear streams and ocean. I was excited to feel my energy and stamina build, as well as to watch how my body responded in new ways. I took pleasure in the new me. This trip gave me the much-needed time to reflect upon my life, and celebrate my new beginning.

One morning as I got ready to hike, I picked up my necklace with the heart pendant. I quickly turned it over and read the inscription on the back, as I had so many times before: "Boldly go into the great and vast unknown." I thought about the past thirty years, and all the challenges I had endured. As I shook my head and sighed, I realized that I had boldly and brilliantly gone into the great and vast unknown, on a journey to recover my health. I had learned about and experienced things that are not readily known or accepted. This was one adventure I was happy to have behind me. A feeling of appreciation welled up in me as I thought about my biological dentist, and how, through his work, I have been given a chance to live the life I have always dreamed of living.

I looked into the mirror and smiled. For the first time in a long time, I liked what I saw. A woman who had a healthy overall glow, rosy cheeks and clear, laughing blue eyes stared back at me. Her eyes were full of wisdom and empathy. I watched the reflection of myself as I held my heart pendant necklace up to my neck, now smooth and without any lumps or bumps. I hesitated before I secured it around my neck. My husband broke my train of thought as he called out to me. Both he and the Wiggs were ready to go hiking. I pushed aside the feeling of hesitation and quickly fastened the chain.

After we returned from our day of exploring new trails, I got ready for a shower. As I removed the necklace from around my neck, I gasped in horror. The pendant was gone! I felt an uncomfortable sinking feeling inside my gut as I stood holding the chain. The next week I retraced my steps, but I never found it. When we returned to Sedona, I visited the shop where my husband had purchased it and told the owner what had happened. She said that she did not have another heart pendant, and did not know if the artist had any others. But she had an idea. While I waited, she called the artist and asked if she would make me another. The artist said yes, but she had a stipulation: I must come up with the inscription for her to engrave on the back.

I went home and took Wiggs on a walk to clear my mind. I felt happy, with a deep sense of contentment, as I watched the glowing colors of the red rocks and the dark-green scrub brush huddled on the edge of the cliffs. I began to think about what I wanted to have inscribed on the back of my new pendant. I wanted the inscription to reflect my new beginning, and the endless possibilities that I could create. I wanted the inscription to express my joy at being able to tap into my potential. I wanted to celebrate the unconditional love I was now able to feel for myself, for my body and for life. I felt very inspired. As I walked up the hill, an idea popped into my mind. I knew exactly how the inscription on the back of that pendant would read.

I decided not to tell anyone what I had decided upon. Several weeks later, I got a phone call from the store's owner telling me that the necklace had arrived. I felt a great sense of excitement as my husband drove me down to the store. The parking lot was full of out-of-state cars, with tourists enjoying the beautiful weather. As we parked, I noticed that the car next to us had a Texas license plate. I laughed. We entered the festive courtyard filled with colorful Mexican tile, plants and flowers. Butterflies and moths moved freely through the airy space. The water from the fountain in the center danced as the sunlight made the water sparkle. Two young boys disturbed the quiet as they raced through the courtyard with peals of laughter, tossing a red ball back and forth between them. I made my way quickly over to the shop as my anticipation mounted. The clerk greeted us.

A few moments later, I beamed as I held the newly made gold heart pendant tightly in my hand. I admired the new gold chain, this time more substantial, that the artist had sent along with the pendant. Slowly, I let go of my clasped fingers and looked carefully at the pendant's several small semi-precious stones, embedded into the surface with the moon, the cut-out gold stars and the various engraved shapes. Turning it over with great care, I saw the inscription. It made me smile. In a feminine script, it read:

"And she lived happily ever after."

Appendix A

MY DENTIST®
2045 S. VINEYARD RD #153
MESA, AZ 85210
(480) 833-2232

Date: 6.4.2013

Dear Kimberly

Please find enclosed:

1. X Your results from the **HEAD AND NECK LAB** Biopsy

2. ____ Your results from the **Clifford Materials Reactivity Test** has been received.

Your biopsy for #1 Upper Right 3RD molar showed:

1. ____ The **osteonecrosis** we expected to find in this type of lesion.

2. ____ The **osteomyelitis** we expected to find in this type of lesion.

3. ____ The **ischemia** we would expect to find in this type of lesion.

4. ____ Please call our office at (480) 833-2232 to set up an appointment. Our Business hours are Monday- Thursday 8-5pm. There are some findings on the report we would like to discuss with you in more detail.

5. ____

OTHER Myospherulosis - w/ foreign body-type granulomatous reaction to oil lipid containing material

If you have any questions or concerns please contact our office at your earliest convenience.

RESULTS REVIEWED BY DR.MARGOLIS

[signature]

Oral & Maxillofacial Diagnostics

A Biopsy Service of the University of Texas School of Dentistry at Houston

Department of Diagnostic and Biomedical Sciences, Room 6110, 7500 Cambridge, Houston, TX 77054

Phone: 713-486-4411; Fax: 713-486-0415; Director: Nadarajah.Vigneswaran@uth.tmc.edu

REPORT #UTDB 2013-1577

Surgery Date: 4/23/2013
Date Received: 5/2/2013
Date Completed: 5/16/2013

DOCTOR:
Michael D. Margolis, DDS
2045 S. Vineyard Rd. Suite 153
Mesa, Arizona 85210
U.S.A.
(480) 833-2232
Fax: (480) 833-3062

PATIENT:
Kimberly Miles-Davis

Source of Specimen (location): Maxilla, posterior, 3rd molar area **Area:** Right

Clinical Diagnosis: NICO, crystallized bone, fatty tissue

Gross Description of Tissue Received:
The specimen was received in a container of formalin identified as #1 and consists of multiple fragments of hard and soft tissue, irregular in shape, tan to dark brown in color, which measure in aggregate 12 x 9 x 2-mm. The specimen is submitted in total pending decalcification. (MS:tr)

Microscopic Description:
Sections show thick and thin bony trabeculae with microcracks and excess cement lines. The bone appears viable, as is a fragment of cortical bone. Available fatty marrow shows areas of extensive avascular fibrosis, in one case embedded with moderate to large globular clear spaces with small gray/translucent globular foreign material. Chronic inflammatory cells are seen in response to the foreign material and one area shows the foreign material to extend through a perforation in the overlying thin cortex. There is no evidence of malignancy. (JB,NV:tr)

Microscopic Diagnosis:
Intramedullary fibrous scar
Myospherulosis

Comments:
The foreign material appears to be a dry socket preventive or medicament which has been in place for a long time. (JB,NV:tr)

PATHOLOGIST: ______________________
N. Vigneswaran DMD, Dr.MedDent

305; 311;528.4;
305; ;528.9; 08-13

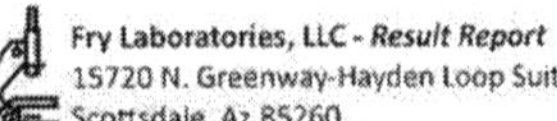

Fry Laboratories, LLC - *Result Report*
15720 N. Greenway-Hayden Loop Suite 3 CLIA#03D1026968 info@frylabs.com
Scottsdale, Az 85260 866.927.8075(p) 480.656.4932(f) 480.292.8457(billing)
FRY LABORATORIES, L.L.C. WWW.FRYLABS.COM

Patient:	Kimberly Miles-Davis	Sample #:	13651-2907	Sample Type:	NICO #32
Doctor:	Michael D. Margolis, DDS	Birth:	06.11.1961	Collection Date:	04.23.2013
Gender:	Female	Prepared By:	DM	Received Date:	05.03.2013

Pan-Bacterial Metagenomics

	Neisseria lactamica	Neisseria flavescens	Streptococcus pseudopneumoniae
■ % Contribution	88.87%	4.97%	1.02%

Description (E-Value)	Genus Antibiotics	Noted Resistance
Neisseria lactamica	Cefotaxime and ceftriaxone.	Penicillin.
Neisseria flavescens	Refer to Neisseria lactamica	Refer to Neisseria lactamica
Streptococcus pseudopneumoniae	Penicillin, amoxicillin, intramuscular benzathine penicillin G, erythromycin, clindamycin, cephalosporins, cephalexin, cefuroxime axetil, and cefdinir	Penicillin, beta-lactams and macrolides

Notes

Sequence Information: 62,801 sequence reads were obtained for the given sample. The longest 1,076 sequences were analyzed and compared to all available prokaryotic species.
Results Confidence Profile: At the provided quality control cut-off it is estimated that >95% of the sequence reads correctly list the genus, while >30% of the sequence reads correctly list the species.
This test uses a kit/reagent designated by the manufacturer as for research use only, not for clinical use. Fry Laboratories, LLC developed this test or some of its components. The performance characteristics of this test are still undergoing validation and verification by Fry Laboratories, LLC. It has not been cleared or approved by the U.S. Food and Drug Administration. No international standard is currently available for the calibration of this assay. The results are not intended to be used as the sole means for clinical diagnosis or patient management decisions. The following genera have been reported as difficult to identify using 16S sequencing: Aeromonas, Bacillus, Bordetella, Burkholderia, Campylobacter, Edwardsiella, Enterobacter, Neisseria, Pseudomonas, and Streptococcus. Sequence results are considered proprietary and Fry Laboratories, LLC may retain patent rights. Patent Pending 2013 Fry Laboratories, LLC. Results are not representative of standard patient test results as it was performed as research. This assay was performed on an investigational and research basis and care should be taken when interpreting these results in combination with diagnostic tests. Completed 05.13.2013. Reviewed by S.Fry, M.D.

Appendix B

Dental DNA

5082 List Drive
Colorado Springs, CO 80919

Telephone: 719-219-2826 Fax: 719-548-8220
TIN: 84-1413291 CLIA#: 06D2019763

Lab Director: Christopher W. Shade, Ph.D, NRCC-EAC Lab Manager: Robert C. Wheeler, BS, MS

Test ID: 000400

PATIENT: Kimberly Miles-Davis

DENTIST: Dr. Michael Margolis

Full View Test

Sample Collected	Sample Received	Sample Tested	Test Reported
06/04/2013	07/19/2013	07/25/2013	07/29/2013

Sample Type: Root Canal #9, #10

The following bacteria were detected in the sample that was submitted for testing:

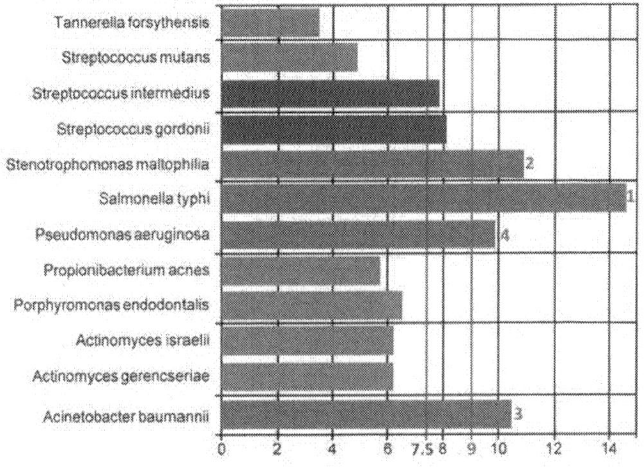

9 or greater indicates a serious risk

Greater than 7.5 but less than 9 indicates a moderate risk

Total Risk Factor, as reported on the chart above, is the sum of the Pathogen Risk Factor and Measured Risk Factor. Total Risk Factor equal to or greater than 9 is considered a serious risk. Total Risk Factor between 7.5 and 9 is considered of moderate risk.

Pathogen Risk Factor is the innate risk of the microbe based on the biology of the organism, disease causation, and microbial antibiotic resistance. It is reported on a scale of 1-10, with 10 being most serious and 1 most benign.

Measured Risk Factor is the value given to the sample taking into account the quantity and configuration of the pathogen DNA. It is reported on a scale of 1-10, with 10 being most serious and 1 most benign.

Interpretation of Results:
These results are from DNA PCR testing, and indicate the presence of targeted foreign DNA. The verbiage is supplied as a courtesy to health care providers to aide in an overall assessment. This information alone should not be used to diagnose or treat a health problem or disease. Consultation with a qualified health care provider is required.

Kimberly Miles-Davis **Dr. Michael Margolis** **Full View Test**

Bacteria	Total Risk Factor	Clinical Significance
Acinetobacter baumannii 3	10.50	**General Description** Acinetobacter is a group of Gram-negative bacteria commonly found in soil and water. While there are numerous species of Acinetobacter and all can cause human disease, Acinetobacter baumannii accounts for about 80% of reported infections. Outbreaks of Acinetobacter infections typically occur in intensive care units and healthcare settings housing very ill patients. Acinetobacter infections rarely occur outside of healthcare settings. **Symptoms of Infection** Acinetobacter causes a variety of diseases, ranging from pneumonia to serious blood or wound infections, and the symptoms vary depending on the tissue infected. Acinetobacter may also "colonize" or live in a patient without causing infection or symptoms, especially in tracheotomy sites or open wounds. **Treatment** Acinetobacter is often resistant to many commonly prescribed antibiotics. Decisions on treatment of infections with Acinetobacter should be made on a case-by-case basis by a healthcare provider. Acinetobacter infection typically occurs in ill patients and can either cause or contribute to death in these patients.
Actinomyces gerencseriae	6.20	**General Description** Actinomyces species are Gram-positive and are normally present in the gingival area. A. gerencseriae is one of the most common causes of infections in dental procedures. **Symptoms of Infection** Many Actinomyces species are opportunistic pathogens of humans and other mammals, particularly in the oral cavity. In rare cases, these bacteria can cause actinomycosis, a disease characterized by the formation of abscesses in the mouth, lungs, or the gastrointestinal tract. **Treatment** Actinomyces bacteria are generally sensitive to penicillin, which is frequently used to treat actinomycosis. In cases of penicillin allergy, doxycycline is used. Sulfonamides such as sulfamethoxazole may be used as an alternative regimen at a total daily dosage of 2-4 grams. Response to therapy is slow and may take months.

Page 2 of 7

Kimberly Miles-Davis		Dr. Michael Margolis	Full View Test
Bacteria	**Total Risk Factor**	**Clinical Significance**	
Actinomyces israelii	6.22	**General Description** Actinomyces species are Gram-positive and are normally present in the gingival area. Actinomyces israelii is one of the most common causes of infections in dental procedures. **Symptoms of Infection** Many Actinomyces species are opportunistic pathogens of humans and other mammals, particularly in the oral cavity. In rare cases, these bacteria can cause actinomycosis, a disease characterized by the formation of abscesses in the mouth, lungs, or the gastrointestinal tract. **Treatment** Actinomyces bacteria are generally sensitive to penicillin, which is frequently used to treat actinomycosis. In cases of penicillin allergy, doxycycline is used. Sulfonamides such as sulfamethoxazole may be used as an alternative regimen at a total daily dosage of 2-4 grams. Response to therapy is slow and may take months.	
Porphyromonas endodontalis	6.50	**General Description** Porphyromonas are Gram-negative, anaerobic, rod-shaped bacteria that produce porphyrin pigments (dark brown/black pigments). Though many members of the Porphyromonas genus are normal flora in the mouth, Porphyromonas endodontalis is only found in patients suffering from periodontal infections. **Symptoms of Infection** Infections frequently cause chronic inflammation of the periodontal tissues. Several post-op infections from oral surgery, most frequently root canals, are caused by Porphyromonas endodontalis. If left untreated, these infections may lead to the infection spreading into the blood or other tissues. **Treatment** Good oral hygiene and proper post-op maintenance of any damaged or exposed tissue in the mouth are the best preventative measures. Studies have shown the Porphyromonas genus may have a resistance to metronidazole, penicillin and other related antibiotics.	

Page 3 of 7

Kimberly Miles-Davis | **Dr. Michael Margolis** | **Full View Test**

Bacteria	Total Risk Factor	Clinical Significance

Propionibacterium acnes — 5.70

General Description

Propionibacterium acnes is the relatively slow-growing, typically aerotolerant anaerobic, Gram-positive bacterium linked to the skin condition acne. This bacterium is largely commensal and part of the skin flora present on most healthy adult humans' skin. Propionibacterium acnes bacteria live deep within follicles and pores, away from the surface of the skin.

Symptoms of Infection

Propionibacterium acnes bacteria secrete many proteins, including several digestive enzymes. The cellular damage, metabolic byproducts and bacterial debris produced by the rapid growth of Propionibacterium acnes in follicles can trigger inflammation. The damage caused by Propionibacterium acnes and the associated inflammation make the affected tissue more susceptible to colonization by opportunistic bacteria, such as Staphylococcus aureus. Propionibacterium acnes is sometimes involved in chronic endophthalmitis, and rarely endocarditis.

Treatment

Propionibacterium acnes has resistance to macrolides, lincosamides, and tetracyclines. It can be treated with erythromycin, clindamycin, doxycycline and minocycline

Pseudomonas aeruginosa — 9.90

4

General Description

Pseudomonas aeruginosa is Gram-negative, aerobic, rod-shaped bacterium with unipolar motility. An opportunistic human pathogen, Pseudomonas aeruginosa is also an opportunistic pathogen of plants. It is found in soil, water, on skin and on most man-made environments throughout the world. Antibiotic resistant strains have become a serious problem in hospitals.

Symptoms of Infection

Pseudomonas aeruginosa is an opportunistic, nosocomial pathogen of immunocompromised individuals. Pseudomonas aeruginosa typically infects the pulmonary tract, urinary tract, burns, wounds, and also causes blood infections. Pseudomonas aeruginosa uses the virulence factor exotoxin A to ADP-ribosylation eukaryotic elongation factor 2 in the host cell. Without elongation factor 2, eukaryotic cells cannot synthesize proteins and undergo apoptosis. The release of intracellular contents induces an immunologic response in immunocompetent patients.

Treatment

The species is naturally resistant to penicillin. It shows susceptibility to gentamicin, ciprofloxacin, antipseudomonal penicillins, carbapenems polymyxins, and monobactams.

Page 4 of 7

Kimberly Miles-Davis	Dr. Michael Margolis	Full View Test

Bacteria	Total Risk Factor	Clinical Significance
Salmonella typhi 1	14.60	**General Description** Salmonella typhi is a Gram-negative, flagellated bacillus. It causes systemic infections and typhoid fever in humans. It has caused many deaths in developing countries where sanitation is poor and is spread through contamination of water and undercooked food **Symptoms of Infection** Symptoms of typhoid fever often include a sudden onset of a high fever, a headache, and nausea. Other common symptoms include loss of appetite, diarrhea, and enlargement of the spleen (depending on where it is located). **Treatment** Strains of MDR (multi-drug resistant) Salmonella have emerged. They show resistance to nalidixic acid and have reduced susceptibility to fluoroquinolones. The species is still susceptible to azithromycin, ampicillin, amoxicillin and ciprofloxacin.
Stenotrophomonas maltophilia 2	10.90	**General Description** Stenotrophomonas maltophilia is an aerobic, nonfermentative, Gram-negative bacterium. It is a tenacious and uncommon bacterium making human infections difficult to treat. **Symptoms of Infection** Stenotrophomonas maltophilia frequently colonizes breathing tubes such as endotracheal, central venous catheters, tracheotomy tubes and indwelling urinary catheters. Infection is usually facilitated by the presence of prosthetic material (plastic or metal), and the most effective treatment is removal of the prosthetic material. In immune compromised patients, Stenotrophomonas maltophilia is a growing source of latent pulmonary infections. **Treatment** Stenotrophomonas maltophilia is naturally resistant to many broad-spectrum antibiotics (including all carbapenems) due to the production of two inducible chromosomal metallo-beta-lactamases (designated L1 and L2). Removal of any synthetic substance or device in the patient is always the most essential step. A broad spectrum antibiotic treatment should be started at the first sign of infection. Co-trimoxazole has been effective, and there is some evidence to suggest regimens of ciprofloxacin, ceftazidime, ceftriaxone, ticarcillin, and clavulanate may also work.

Page 5 of 7

Kimberly Miles-Davis		Dr. Michael Margolis	Full View Test
Bacteria	**Total Risk Factor**	**Clinical Significance**	
Streptococcus gordonii	8.10	**General Description** Streptococcus gordonii are gram positive, nonmotile cocci that are integral members of the human oral flora. Streptococcus gordonii can produce bio-films which other bacterial colonizers can adhere to. This may lead to periodontal infections as pathogenic bacteria are now able to invade new areas of the mouth. **Symptoms of Infection** Streptococcus gordonii also causes bacterial endocarditis by entering the blood stream usually after oral trauma. Once in the blood, Streptococcus gordonii colonizes platelet-fibrin thrombi, and are circulated through the blood stream. From there, it can colonize damaged heart valves leading to further dysfunction of the heart. **Treatment** Streptococcus gordonii shows some antibiotic resistance, but generally is not pathogenic unless it can access the blood stream. Good oral hygiene can diminish the bacteria's presence in the mouth. Proper care of any open wounds in the mouth will also reduce risk of infection. When necessary, infections should be treated with ceftriaxone.	
Streptococcus intermedius	7.83	**General Description** A member of the Streptococcus anginosus group, Streptococcus intermedius is a species of Gram-positive bacteria commonly found in the oropharynx flora and has a proclivity for abscess formation. **Symptoms of Infection** Streptococcus intermedius has a tendency to cause abscess formation most commonly in the liver and brain, but is rarely the etiologic agent in infective endocarditis. Infections are rare in adults with normal functioning immune systems. **Treatment** Streptococcus intermedius, like many Streptococci, is highly resistant to many antibiotics including penicillin, ampicillin, and related drugs, but shows general susceptibility to ceftriaxone.	

Page 6 of 7

Kimberly Miles-Davis		Dr. Michael Margolis	Full View Test
Bacteria	**Total Risk Factor**	**Clinical Significance**	
Streptococcus mutans	4.90	**General Description** Streptococcus mutans is a facultatively anaerobic, Gram-positive cocci commonly found in the human oral cavity. It is a significant contributor to tooth decay, which it accomplishes by producing lactic acid. **Symptoms of Infection** Cavities in the tooth are the most common signs of infections. It has been implicated in certain cardiovascular diseases such as extirpated heart valve tissues and atheromatous plaques. **Treatment** Good oral hygiene should prevent most infections. The growth and spread of S. mutans can also be reduced by the consumption of certain foods such as, green tea, nutmeg and various herbs. It responds to clindamycin and chloramphenicol if a serious infection needs treatment.	
Tannerella forsythensis	3.50	**General Description** Tannerella forsythia is an anaerobic, gram negative species of bacteria of the Cytophaga-Bacteroidetes family and is implicated in periodontal disease. T. forsythia is commonly located on the supragingival tissue and initiates periodontitis by colonizing the subgingival tissue. **Symptoms of Infection** Tannerella forsythia causes periodontal infections and chronic inflammation of tooth supporting tissues which can lead to tooth lose. **Treatment** Tannerella forsythia is susceptible to ampicillin, amoxicillin and doxycycline.	

Page 7 of 7

Appendix C

Dental DNA
5082 List Drive
Colorado Springs, CO 80919

Telephone: 719-219-2826 Fax: 719-548-8220
TIN: 84-1413291 CLIA#: 06D2019763

Lab Director: Christopher W. Shade, Ph.D, NRCC-EAC Lab Manager: Christina L. Romero, MD

Test ID: 001006

PATIENT:	DENTIST:	Full View Test
Kimberly Miles-Davis	**Dr. Michael Margolis**	

Sample Collected	Sample Received	Sample Tested	Test Reported
02/17/2014	02/18/2014	02/21/2014	02/25/2014

Sample Type: Cavitation #16

The following bacteria were detected in the sample that was submitted for testing:

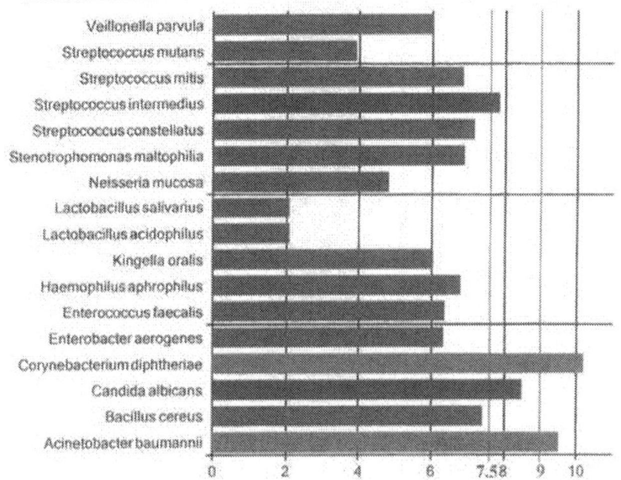

9 or greater indicates a serious risk

Greater than 7.5 but less than 9 indicates a moderate risk

Total Risk Factor, as reported on the chart above, is the sum of the Pathogen Risk Factor and Measured Risk Factor. Total Risk Factor equal to or greater than 9 is considered a serious risk. Total Risk Factor between 7.5 and 9 is considered of moderate risk.

Pathogen Risk Factor is the innate risk of the microbe based on the biology of the organism, disease causation, and microbial antibiotic resistance. It is reported on a scale of 1-10, with 10 being most serious and 1 most benign.

Measured Risk Factor is the value given to the sample taking into account the quantity and configuration of the pathogen DNA. It is reported on a scale of 1-10, with 10 being most serious and 1 most benign.

Interpretation of Results:
These results are from DNA PCR testing, and indicate the presence of targeted foreign DNA. The verbiage is supplied as a courtesy to health care providers to aide in an overall assessment. This information alone should not be used to diagnose or treat a health problem or disease. Consultation with a qualified health care provider is required.

Kimberly Miles-Davis **Dr. Michael Margolis** **Full View Test**

Bacteria	Total Risk Factor	Clinical Significance
Acinetobacter baumannii	9.50	**General Description** Acinetobacter is a group of Gram-negative bacteria commonly found in soil and water. While there are numerous species of Acinetobacter and all can cause human disease, Acinetobacter baumannii accounts for about 80% of reported infections. Outbreaks of Acinetobacter infections typically occur in intensive care units and healthcare settings housing very ill patients. Acinetobacter infections rarely occur outside of healthcare settings. **Symptoms of Infection** Acinetobacter causes a variety of diseases, ranging from pneumonia to serious blood or wound infections, and the symptoms vary depending on the tissue infected. Acinetobacter may also "colonize" or live in a patient without causing infection or symptoms, especially in tracheotomy sites or open wounds. **Treatment** Acinetobacter is often resistant to many commonly prescribed antibiotics. Decisions on treatment of infections with Acinetobacter should be made on a case-by-case basis by a healthcare provider. Acinetobacter infection typically occurs in ill patients and can either cause or contribute to death in these patients.
Bacillus cereus	7.40	**General Description** Bacillus cereus is a Gram-positive, rod-shaped bacterium which generally lives in the soil. Bacillus cereus is responsible for a minority of food borne illnesses (2-5%), causing severe nausea, vomiting and diarrhea. The food borne illness occurs due to survival of the bacterial endospores when food is improperly cooked. **Symptoms of Infection** Bacterial growth results in production of enterotoxins, ingestion of which leads to two types of illness, diarrheal and emetic (vomiting) syndrome. **Treatment** The disease is usually self limiting but in cases of severe infections it should be treated with antibiotics. Is resistant to beta-lactam antibiotics, but is usually susceptible to treatment with clindamycin, vancomycin, gentamicin, chloramphenicol, and erythromycin.

Page 2 of 8

Kimberly Miles-Davis		Dr. Michael Margolis	Full View Test
Bacteria	**Total Risk Factor**	**Clinical Significance**	
Candida albicans	8.50	**General Description** Candida albicans is commensal and a constituent of the normal flora, and it lives in 80% of the human population without causing harmful effects. Systemic fungal infections (fungemias) including those by Candida albicans have emerged as important causes of morbidity and mortality in immunocompromised patients. Candida albicans biofilms may form on the surface of implantable medical devices. **Symptoms of Infection** An infection in the bloodstream can affect the kidneys, heart, lungs, eyes, or other organs causing high fever, chills, anemia, and sometimes a rash or shock. Candida can cause the following problems depending upon the organ infected: in the kidneys can cause blood in the urine, in the heart can cause murmurs and valve damage, in the lungs can cause bloody sputum (mucus discharge), in the eyes can cause pain and blurred vision, in the brain can cause seizures and acute changes in mental function or behavior like lactobacillus does – as yeast, keeps microbes in balance – change in pH by Hg and sugar yeast shifts to fungus – Antibioitic shifts yeast to fungus **Treatment** Treatment commonly includes: amphotericin B, caspofungin, or fluconazole for systemic infections; fluconazole or caspofungin for oral or esophageal infections; and topical azole for vaginal infections.	
Corynebacterium diphtheriae	10.20	**General Description** Corynebacterium diphtheriae is a pathogenic bacterium that is spread by direct physical contact and causes diphtheria. It is a Gram-positive, highly pleomorphic facultative anaerobic organism with no particular arrangement. **Symptoms of Infection** Diphtheria is an upper respiratory tract illness. It is characterized by sore throat, low fever, and an adherent membrane on the tonsils, pharynx, and/or nasal cavity. A milder form of diphtheria can be restricted to the skin. Less common consequences include myocarditis and peripheral neuropathy. **Treatment** Corynebacterium diphtheriae is sensitive to the majority of antibiotics, such as the penicillins, ampicillin, cephalosporins, quinolones, chloramphenicol, tetracyclines, cefuroxime and trimethoprim.	

Page 3 of 8

Kimberly Miles-Davis | Dr. Michael Margolis | Full View Test

Bacteria	Total Risk Factor	Clinical Significance
Enterobacter aerogenes	6.30	**General Description** Enterobacter aerogenes is a Gram-negative, rod-shaped bacterium. Enterobacter aerogenes is found in the human gastrointestinal tract and does not generally cause disease in healthy individuals. **Symptoms of Infection** Enterobacter aerogenes is not normally pathogenic, but may cause various types of infection in immune compromised individuals. Antibiotic resistant strains are becoming increasingly common nosocomial pathogens. **Treatment** The major classes of antibiotics used to manage infections include the beta-lactams, carbapenems, the fluoroquinolones, the aminoglycosides, and TMP-SMZ. Because most Enterobacter species are either resistant to many antibiotics or can develop resistance during antimicrobial therapy, the choice of appropriate antimicrobial agents can be complicated.
Enterococcus faecalis	6.37	**General Description** Enterococcus faecalis is a Gram-positive, commensal bacterium inhabiting the gastrointestinal tracts of humans and other mammals **Symptoms of Infection** Enterococcus faecalis can cause endocarditis and bacteremia, urinary tract infections (UTI), meningitis, and other infections in humans. **Treatment** Enterococcus faecalis is resistant to many commonly used antimicrobial agents (aminoglycosides, aztreonam, cephalosporins, clindamycin, the semisynthetic penicillins nafcillin and oxacillin, and trimethoprim-sulfamethoxazole). Resistance to vancomycin in Enterococcus faecalis is becoming more common. Treatment options for vancomycin-resistant Enterococcus faecalis include linezolid and daptomycin, although ampicillin is preferred if the bacteria are susceptible.
Haemophilus aphrophilus	6.80	**General Description** Haemophilus aphrophilus is an oral fastidious Gram-negative commensal bacterium with low pathogenicity **Symptoms of Infection** Haemophilus aphrophilus infections are often in the bones and joints. They can manifest as osteomyelitis, discitis, epidural abscess, spondylodiscitis, septic arthritis and prevertebral infection. H. aphrophilus has been reported to cause rare instances of endocarditis. **Treatment** Antimicrobial therapy, such as a beta-lactam/beta-lactamase inhibitor, ceftriaxone, cefotaxime or fluoroquinolone have been successful.

Page 4 of 8

Kimberly Miles-Davis		Dr. Michael Margolis	Full View Test

Bacteria	Total Risk Factor	Clinical Significance
Kingella oralis	6.05	**General Description** Kingella oralis is a strictly aerobic, Gram-negative diplococci and typically do not have flagella. **Symptoms of Infection** Kingella oralis are mammalian commensals, often found on the surface of teeth. In rare cases, Kingella oralis may be an opportunistic pathogen that can cause localized infections and meningitis. **Treatment** It is not usually necessary to treat a Kingella oralis infection with antibiotics. However, in immune compromised patents or in cases of meningitis, the preferred treatment is ceftriaxone or penicillin.
Lactobacillus acidophilus	2.10	**General Description** Lactobacillus acidophilus is a Gram-positive bacillus that occurs naturally in the human and animal gastrointestinal tract, mouth, and vagina. Lactobacillus acidophilus is a homofermentative species, fermenting sugars into lactic acid, and grows vigorously at low pH values. **Symptoms of Infection** Lactobacillus acidophilus is a common probiotic that may reduce the risk of infection and improve overall health. It has been associated with dental carries most likely because it creates an acidic environment in the mouth. This acidic environment can degrade mineralized tissue such as teeth. **Treatment** Lactobacillus acidophilus is an essential member of normal human flora. Good oral hygiene will prevent large colonies from acidifying the mouth.
Lactobacillus salivarius	2.10	**General Description** Lactobacillus salivarius is a Gram-positive, facultatively anaerobic rod-shaped bacteria. It is an important part of normal, human bacterial flora, and is frequently taken as a probiotic supplement. **Symptoms of Infection** Lactobacillus salivarius is rarely pathogenic, though it has been associated with other bacteria in dental carries. The Lactobacillus genus produce acid as part of their metabolic processes, which may cause some demineralization of the teeth. **Treatment** Good oral hygiene will prevent acidification of the mouth by Lactobacillus salivarius.

Page 5 of 8

Kimberly Miles-Davis | **Dr. Michael Margolis** | **Full View Test**

Bacteria	Total Risk Factor	Clinical Significance
Neisseria mucosa	4.80	**General Description** Neisseria mucosa is a facultatively anaerobic, Gram-negative, diplococci that resemble coffee beans when viewed microscopically. Generally a non-pathogenic, commensal organism, Neisseria mucosa colonizes the mucosal surfaces of the human mouth. **Symptoms of Infection** Neisseria mucosa can cause localized wound infections or rarely, endocarditis when trauma allows it access to the blood stream. **Treatment** Neisseria mucosa is susceptible to many antibiotics, but is sometimes penicillin resistant. If it is resistant, it should be treated with ceftriaxone.
Stenotrophomonas maltophilia	6.90	**General Description** Stenotrophomonas maltophilia is an aerobic, nonfermentative, Gram-negative bacterium. It is a tenacious and uncommon bacterium making human infections difficult to treat. **Symptoms of Infection** Stenotrophomonas maltophilia frequently colonizes breathing tubes such as endotracheal, central venous catheters, tracheotomy tubes and indwelling urinary catheters. Infection is usually facilitated by the presence of prosthetic material (plastic or metal), and the most effective treatment is removal of the prosthetic material. In immune compromised patients, Stenotrophomonas maltophilia is a growing source of latent pulmonary infections. **Treatment** Stenotrophomonas maltophilia is naturally resistant to many broad-spectrum antibiotics (including all carbapenems) due to the production of two inducible chromosomal metallo-beta-lactamases (designated L1 and L2). Removal of any synthetic substance or device in the patient is always the most essential step. A broad spectrum antibiotic treatment should be started at the first sign of infection. Co-trimoxazole has been effective, and there is some evidence to suggest regimens of ciprofloxacin, ceftazidime, ceftriaxone, ticarcillin, and clavulanate may also work.

Kimberly Miles-Davis		Dr. Michael Margolis	Full View Test
Bacteria	Total Risk Factor	Clinical Significance	
Streptococcus constellatus	7.15	**General Description** Streptococcus constellatus is a Gram-positive, non-spore forming, non-motile cocci that are part of the normal flora in the oral cavity, urogenital region, and intestinal tract. **Symptoms of Infection** Can cause abscess formation in the upper body and respiratory tract, and is the most common cause of brain and liver abscesses. It has also been found to be involved with pulmonary exacerbations in cystic fibrosis patients. Healthy, non-immune compromised adults rarely get infections. **Treatment** Streptococcus constellatus is generally resistant to penicillin but susceptible to other forms of antibiotic treatment such as ceftriaxone. Abscess and infected tissue should be removed if infection is severe.	
Streptococcus intermedius	7.83	**General Description** A member of the Streptococcus anginosus group. Streptococcus intermedius is a species of Gram-positive bacteria commonly found in the oropharynx flora and has a proclivity for abscess formation. **Symptoms of Infection** Streptococcus intermedius has a tendency to cause abscess formation most commonly in the liver and brain, but is rarely the etiologic agent in infective endocarditis. Infections are rare in adults with normal functioning immune systems. **Treatment** Streptococcus intermedius, like many Streptococci, is highly resistant to many antibiotics including penicillin, ampicillin, and related drugs, but shows general susceptibility to ceftriaxone.	
Streptococcus mitis	6.85	**General Description** Streptococcus Mitis is a Gram-positive, facultatively anaerobic and catalase negative coccus. Streptococcus mitis is a commensal bacteria commonly found in the mouth. It most often colonizes the outer surface of teeth as well as mucous membranes. **Symptoms of Infection** Streptococcus mitis is usually an etiologic agent in odontogenic infection and endocarditis. While healthy people rarely contract infections, there is evidence that inflammation caused by Streptococcus mitis may result in cardiac complications even in normal individuals. The major interaction in the pathogenesis of infective endocarditis is the direct binding of bacteria to platelets. **Treatment** Good oral hygiene helps prevent infections, including those of the cardiovascular system. Streptococcus mitis is often penicillin resistant but shows susceptibility to clindamycin and chloramphenicol.	

Page 7 of 8

Kimberly Miles-Davis		Dr. Michael Margolis	Full View Test
Bacteria	**Total Risk Factor**	**Clinical Significance**	
Streptococcus mutans	3.90	**General Description** Streptococcus mutans is a facultatively anaerobic, Gram-positive cocci commonly found in the human oral cavity. It is a significant contributor to tooth decay, which it accomplishes by producing lactic acid. **Symptoms of Infection** Cavities in the tooth are the most common signs of infections. It has been implicated in certain cardiovascular diseases such as extirpated heart valve tissues and atheromatous plaques. **Treatment** Good oral hygiene should prevent most infections. The growth and spread of S. mutans can also be reduced by the consumption of certain foods such as, green tea, nutmeg and various herbs. It responds to clindamycin and chloramphenicol if a serious infection needs treatment.	
Veillonella parvula	6.01	**General Description** Veillonella parvula is a Gram-negative, strictly anaerobic, non-spore-forming cocci. It is found in the gut of humans and dental plaque. It is part of the normal oral flora, and is generally considered non-pathogenic. While rarely pathogenic itself, it is able to coaggregate with other organisms, namely Streptococcus mutans, to form dental plaques. **Symptoms of Infection** There is little evidence of Veillonella parvula being the main etiological agent in disease, but it has been associated with cases of meningitis, osteomyelitis, and periodontal disease. **Treatment** In the rare case of infection, it is susceptible to penicillin.	

Page 8 of 8

Dental DNA
5082 List Drive
Colorado Springs, CO 80919

Telephone: 719-219-2826 | Fax: 719-548-8220
TIN: 84-1413291 | CLIA#: 06D2019763

Lab Director: Christopher W. Shade, Ph.D, NRCC-EAC | Lab Manager: Christina L. Romero, MD

Test ID: 001009

PATIENT: **Kimberly Miles-Davis**

DENTIST: **Dr. Michael Margolis**

Full View Test

Sample Collected	Sample Received	Sample Tested	Test Reported
02/17/2014	02/18/2014	02/21/2014	02/25/2014

Sample Type: Cavitation #17

The following bacteria were detected in the sample that was submitted for testing:

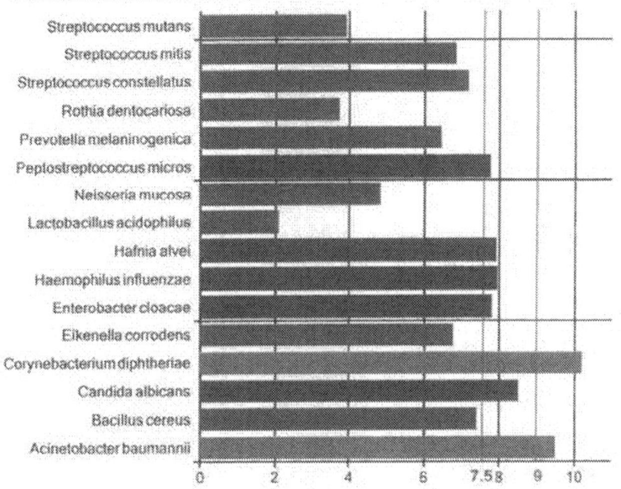

9 or greater indicates a serious risk

Greater than 7.5 but less than 9 indicates a moderate risk

Total Risk Factor, as reported on the chart above, is the sum of the Pathogen Risk Factor and Measured Risk Factor. Total Risk Factor equal to or greater than 9 is considered a serious risk. Total Risk Factor between 7.5 and 9 is considered of moderate risk.

Pathogen Risk Factor is the innate risk of the microbe based on the biology of the organism, disease causation, and microbial antibiotic resistance. It is reported on a scale of 1-10, with 10 being most serious and 1 most benign.

Measured Risk Factor is the value given to the sample taking into account the quantity and configuration of the pathogen DNA. It is reported on a scale of 1-10, with 10 being most serious and 1 most benign.

Interpretation of Results:
These results are from DNA PCR testing, and indicate the presence of targeted foreign DNA. The verbiage is supplied as a courtesy to health care providers to aide in an overall assessment. This information alone should not be used to diagnose or treat a health problem or disease. Consultation with a qualified health care provider is required.

Kimberly Miles-Davis		Dr. Michael Margolis	Full View Test
Bacteria	**Total Risk Factor**	**Clinical Significance**	
Acinetobacter baumannii	9.50	**General Description** Acinetobacter is a group of Gram-negative bacteria commonly found in soil and water. While there are numerous species of Acinetobacter and all can cause human disease, Acinetobacter baumannii accounts for about 80% of reported infections. Outbreaks of Acinetobacter infections typically occur in intensive care units and healthcare settings housing very ill patients. Acinetobacter infections rarely occur outside of healthcare settings. **Symptoms of Infection** Acinetobacter causes a variety of diseases, ranging from pneumonia to serious blood or wound infections, and the symptoms vary depending on the tissue infected. Acinetobacter may also "colonize" or live in a patient without causing infection or symptoms, especially in tracheotomy sites or open wounds. **Treatment** Acinetobacter is often resistant to many commonly prescribed antibiotics. Decisions on treatment of infections with Acinetobacter should be made on a case-by-case basis by a healthcare provider. Acinetobacter infection typically occurs in ill patients and can either cause or contribute to death in these patients.	
Bacillus cereus	7.40	**General Description** Bacillus cereus is a Gram-positive, rod-shaped bacterium which generally lives in the soil. Bacillus cereus is responsible for a minority of food borne illnesses (2-5%), causing severe nausea, vomiting and diarrhea. The food borne illness occurs due to survival of the bacterial endospores when food is improperly cooked. **Symptoms of Infection** Bacterial growth results in production of enterotoxins, ingestion of which leads to two types of illness, diarrheal and emetic (vomiting) syndrome. **Treatment** The disease is usually self limiting but in cases of severe infections it should be treated with antibiotics. Is resistant to beta-lactam antibiotics, but is usually susceptible to treatment with clindamycin, vancomycin, gentamicin, chloramphenicol, and erythromycin.	

Page 2 of 7

Kimberly Miles-Davis		Dr. Michael Margolis	Full View Test

Bacteria	Total Risk Factor	Clinical Significance
Candida albicans	8.50	**General Description** Candida albicans is commensal and a constituent of the normal flora, and it lives in 80% of the human population without causing harmful effects. Systemic fungal infections (fungemias) including those by Candida albicans have emerged as important causes of morbidity and mortality in immunocompromised patients. Candida albicans biofilms may form on the surface of implantable medical devices. **Symptoms of Infection** An infection in the bloodstream can affect the kidneys, heart, lungs, eyes, or other organs causing high fever, chills, anemia, and sometimes a rash or shock. Candida can cause the following problems depending upon the organ infected: in the kidneys can cause blood in the urine, in the heart can cause murmurs and valve damage, in the lungs can cause bloody sputum (mucus discharge), in the eyes can cause pain and blurred vision, in the brain can cause seizures and acute changes in mental function or behavior like lactobacillus does – as yeast, keeps microbes in balance – change in pH by Hg and sugar yeast shifts to fungus – Antibioitic shifts yeast to fungus **Treatment** Treatment commonly includes: amphotericin B, caspofungin, or fluconazole for systemic infections; fluconazole or caspofungin for oral or esophageal infections; and topical azole for vaginal infections.
Corynebacterium diphtheriae	10.20	**General Description** Corynebacterium diphtheriae is a pathogenic bacterium that is spread by direct physical contact and causes diphtheria. It is a Gram-positive, highly pleomorphic facultative anaerobic organism with no particular arrangement. **Symptoms of Infection** Diphtheria is an upper respiratory tract illness. It is characterized by sore throat, low fever, and an adherent membrane on the tonsils, pharynx, and/or nasal cavity. A milder form of diphtheria can be restricted to the skin. Less common consequences include myocarditis and peripheral neuropathy. **Treatment** Corynebacterium diphtheriae is sensitive to the majority of antibiotics, such as the penicillins, ampicillin, cephalosporins, quinolones, chloramphenicol, tetracyclines, cefuroxime and trimethoprim.

Page 3 of 7

Kimberly Miles-Davis		Dr. Michael Margolis	Full View Test
Bacteria	**Total Risk Factor**	**Clinical Significance**	
Eikenella corrodens	6.75	**General Description** Eikenella corrodens is a fastidious Gram-negative, facultatively anaerobic bacillus. **Symptoms of Infection** Eikenella corrodens is a commensal bacterium of the human mouth and upper respiratory tract. It is an unusual cause of disease but may be found mixed with other bacteria in infection sites. Infections most often occur in patients with cancers of the head and neck. It is also common in human bite wound infections. **Treatment** Eikenella corrodens can be treated with penicillins, cephalosporins, or tetracyclines. It is innately resistant to macrolides (e.g., erythromycin), clindamycin, and metronidazole.	
Enterobacter cloacae	7.80	**General Description** Enterobacter cloacae is a clinically significant Gram-negative, facultatively-anaerobic, rod-shaped bacterium. **Symptoms of Infection** Enterobacter cloacae are nosocomial pathogens that can cause a range of infections such as bacteremia, lower respiratory tract infection, skin and soft tissue infections, urinary tract infections, endocarditis, intra-abdominal infections, septic arthritis, osteomyelitis, and ophthalmic infections. This organism affects mostly the vulnerable age groups such as the elderly and the young. **Treatment** These bacteria are highly resistant to antibiotics such as penicillin, and third generation cephalosporins. Successful treatment with cefepime and gentamicin has been reported.	
Haemophilus influenzae	7.95	**General Description** Haemophilus influenza is a Gram-negative, rod-shaped bacterium that is a facultative anaerobe. It was mistakenly considered to be the cause of influenza until 1933. **Symptoms of Infection** Haemophilus influenzae is a opportunistic pathogen that manifests as bacteremia, pneumonia, and acute bacterial meningitis. On occasion, it causes cellulitis, osteomyelitis, epiglottitis, and infectious arthritis. **Treatment** Haemophilus influenzae is resistant to the penicillin family of antibiotics. In severe cases, cefotaxime and ceftriaxone were given intravenously. In more common cases, ampicillin, sulbactam, cephalosporins of the second and third generation and fluoroquinolones are preferred.	

Page 4 of 7

Kimberly Miles-Davis		Dr. Michael Margolis	Full View Test

Bacteria	Total Risk Factor	Clinical Significance
Hafnia alvei	7.90	**General Description** Hafnia alvei is a Gram-negative, facultatively anaerobic, rod-shaped bacterium. Hafnia alvei is a commensal of the human gastrointestinal tract and not normally pathogenic, but may cause disease in immune compromised patients. **Symptoms of Infection** Hafnia alvei is associated with gastroenteritis, meningitis, bacteremia, pneumonia, nosocomial wound infections and endophthalmitis. **Treatment** Hafnia alvei is often resistant to multiple antibiotics, including the aminopenicillins. However, netilmicin, ciprofloxacin, and imipenem are usually effective. Additionally, piperacillin, ceftriaxone and ceftazidime have been reported to be effective.
Lactobacillus acidophilus	2.10	**General Description** Lactobacillus acidophilus is a Gram-positive bacillus that occurs naturally in the human and animal gastrointestinal tract, mouth, and vagina. Lactobacillus acidophilus is a homofermentative species, fermenting sugars into lactic acid, and grows vigorously at low pH values. **Symptoms of Infection** Lactobacillus acidophilus is a common probiotic that may reduce the risk of infection and improve overall health. It has been associated with dental carries most likely because it creates an acidic environment in the mouth. This acidic environment can degrade mineralized tissue such as teeth. **Treatment** Lactobacillus acidophilus is an essential member of normal human flora. Good oral hygiene will prevent large colonies from acidifying the mouth.
Neisseria mucosa	4.80	**General Description** Neisseria mucosa is a facultatively anaerobic, Gram-negative, diplococci that resemble coffee beans when viewed microscopically. Generally a non-pathogenic, commensal organism, Neisseria mucosa colonizes the mucosal surfaces of the human mouth. **Symptoms of Infection** Neisseria mucosa can cause localized wound infections or rarely, endocarditis when trauma allows it access to the blood stream. **Treatment** Neisseria mucosa is susceptible to many antibiotics, but is sometimes penicillin resistant. If it is resistant, it should be treated with ceftriaxone.

Kimberly Miles-Davis | **Dr. Michael Margolis** | **Full View Test**

Bacteria	Total Risk Factor	Clinical Significance
Peptostreptococcus micros	7.73	**General Description** Peptostreptococcus micros is an anaerobic, Gram-positive, slow-growing non-spore forming bacteria with increasing resistance to antimicrobial drugs. It is a commensal organism, living predominantly in the mouth, skin, gastrointestinal, vagina and urinary tracts. **Symptoms of Infection** Under immune suppressed or traumatic conditions, Peptostreptococcus micros can become pathogenic. The organism can cause brain, liver, breast, and lung abscesses, as well as generalized necrotizing soft tissue infections. **Treatment** Peptostreptococcus micros shows resistance to many antimicrobials including, aminoglycosides, and trimethoprim-sulfamethazine. It has been susceptible to newer quinolones.
Prevotella melaninogenica	6.42	**General Description** Prevotella melaninogenica is a Gram-negative, anaerobic, non-spore forming coccobacilli frequently found in the human oral cavity. It is an opportunistic pathogen often involved in polymicrobial infections of the mouth and upper respiratory tract. Prevotella melaninogenica colonies produce a black pigment that can clearly be seen in active infection sites. **Symptoms of Infection** Prevotella melaninogenica can be commonly found and isolated from severe anaerobic infections of the intestinal tract, the female genital tract, the upper and lower respiratory tract and the sites of osteomyelitis. Prevotella melaninogenica can produce transmissible, polymicrobial, subcutaneous infections in the mouth. **Treatment** Prevotella melaninogenica has some natural antibiotic resistance. It can be successfully treated with: metronidazole, amoxicillin/clavulanate, ureidopenicillins, carbapenems, cephalosporins, clindamycin, and chloramphenicol.
Rothia dentocariosa	3.70	**General Description** Rothia dentocariosa is a species of Gram-positive, round- to rod-shaped bacteria that is part of the normal community of microbes residing in the mouth and respiratory tract. First isolated from dental caries, Rothia dentocariosa is largely benign, but can cause disease. **Symptoms of Infection** Rothia dentocariosa is largely a benign part of the normal flora within the human mouth. In rare instances it causes disease, primarily endocarditis, but this infection always occurs in individuals with previous cardiac trauma or abnormalities. **Treatment** Rothia dentocariosa is susceptible to most antibiotics including penicillin.

Page 6 of 7

Kimberly Miles-Davis | **Dr. Michael Margolis** | **Full View Test**

Bacteria	Total Risk Factor	Clinical Significance
Streptococcus constellatus	7.15	**General Description** Streptococcus constellatus is a Gram-positive, non-spore forming, non-motile cocci that are part of the normal flora in the oral cavity, urogenital region, and intestinal tract. **Symptoms of Infection** Can cause abscess formation in the upper body and respiratory tract, and is the most common cause of brain and liver abscesses. It has also been found to be involved with pulmonary exacerbations in cystic fibrosis patients. Healthy, non-immune compromised adults rarely get infections. **Treatment** Streptococcus constellatus is generally resistant to penicillin but susceptible to other forms of antibiotic treatment such as ceftriaxone. Abscess and infected tissue should be removed if infection is severe.
Streptococcus mitis	6.85	**General Description** Streptococcus Mitis is a Gram-positive, facultatively anaerobic and catalase negative coccus. Streptococcus mitis is a commensal bacteria commonly found in the mouth. It most often colonizes the outer surface of teeth as well as mucous membranes. **Symptoms of Infection** Streptococcus mitis is usually an etiologic agent in odontogenic infection and endocarditis. While healthy people rarely contract infections, there is evidence that inflammation caused by Streptococcus mitis may result in cardiac complications even in normal individuals. The major interaction in the pathogenesis of infective endocarditis is the direct binding of bacteria to platelets. **Treatment** Good oral hygiene helps prevent infections, including those of the cardiovascular system. Streptococcus mitis is often penicillin resistant but shows susceptibility to clindamycin and chloramphenicol.
Streptococcus mutans	3.90	**General Description** Streptococcus mutans is a facultatively anaerobic, Gram-positive cocci commonly found in the human oral cavity. It is a significant contributor to tooth decay, which it accomplishes by producing lactic acid. **Symptoms of Infection** Cavities in the tooth are the most common signs of infections. It has been implicated in certain cardiovascular diseases such as extirpated heart valve tissues and atheromatous plaques. **Treatment** Good oral hygiene should prevent most infections. The growth and spread of S. mutans can also be reduced by the consumption of certain foods such as, green tea, nutmeg and various herbs. It responds to clindamycin and chloramphenicol if a serious infection needs treatment.

Endnotes

1 Ann Allen created this pendant as part of her Goddess series. The pieces are engraved with symbols to reflect a woman's personal power.

2 According to Dr. Levy, it is illegal for a dentist and a medical doctor to practice together because there is no board that can oversee both professions. Hal A. Huggins and Thomas E. Levy, *Uninformed Consent, The Hidden Dangers in Dental Care* (Virginia: Hampton Roads Publishing, 1999), 121-22.

3 Mark A. Breiner, *Whole Body Dentistry, A Complete Guide to Understanding the Impact of Dentistry on Total Health* (Connecticut: Quantum Health Press, 2011), 187.

4 Dr. Haley describes the toxicity of mercury, root canals and jawbone osteonecrosis and how the toxicity effects enzymes. Boyd Haley, "1998." Filmed (1998), meeting of the International Academy of Oral Medicine and Toxicology. YouTube video, 1:08:07. Posted July 5, 2015. www.youtube.com/watch?v=eNNu_t9VvD8.

5 Breiner, 184.

6 From *Miss Rumphius* by Barbara Cooney, copyright © 1982 by Barbara Cooney Porter. Used by permission of

Viking Children's Books, an imprint of Penguin Young Readers Group, a division of Penguin Random House LLC.

7 Oxford Dictionaries, s.v. "health," accessed February 13, 2016, http://www.oxforddictionaries.com/us/definition/american_english/health.

8 "WHO Definition of Health," http://www.who.int/about/mission/en/.

9 Dr. George Canguilheim, *The Normal and the Pathological,* trans. Carolyn R. Fawcett (New York: Zone Books, 1991).

10 James L. Wilson, *Adrenal Fatigue: The 21st Century Stress Syndrome* (California: Smart Publications, 2001).

11 Alan Christianson, *The Adrenal Reset Diet* (New York: Harmony Books, 2014).

12 Ibid.

13 A buildup of tartar around the teeth can be an indication of a calcium imbalance. This imbalance is a reflection of an overall imbalance in the pH of the body. The pH is the measurement of the acidity or alkalinity of a substance or solution. For cells to function optimally, the body must maintain proper pH. The demineralization of tooth enamel and bone is caused by a pH of 5.5 or below. Breiner, 130-134.

14 Weston A. Price, *Nutrition and Physical Degeneration* (California: Price-Pottinger Nutrition Foundation, 2008), 430-432.

[15] George E. Meinig, *Root Canal Cover-Up, A Founder of the Association of Root Canal Specialists Discovers Evidence that Root Canals Damage your Health — Learn What to Do* (California: Price-Pottenger Nutrition Foundation, 2008),14. Since 1952 the Price-Pottenger Nutrition Foundation owns and preserves the documented research of Dr. Weston Price. Quotation used with permission from the foundation, www.ppnf.org. Contact: info@ppnf.org; 800-366-3748.

[16] John W. Moore and John H. Brekke, "Foreign Body Giant Cell Reaction Related to Placement of Tetracycline-Treated Polylactic Acid: Report of 18 Cases," Journal of Oral Maxillofacial Surgeons 48 (1990): 808-812. Accessed April 27, 2014.

[17] Ibid.

[18] Roger E. Alexander, "Dental Extraction Wound Management: A Case Against Medicating Postextraction Sockets," Journal of Oral Maxillofacial Surgeons 58 (2000): 538-551. Accessed April 27, 2014, doi:10. 1053/ jo. 2000.5532.

[19] Ibid., 545.

[20] George E. Meinig, 168.

[21] Robert Kulacz and Thomas E. Levy, *The Roots of Disease, Connecting Dentistry and Medicine* (Indiana: Xlibris Corporation, 2002), 88-91.

[22] Hal A. Huggins and Thomas E. Levy, 83.

[23] Ibid., 200.

[24] Robert Kulacz and Thomas E. Levy, The Toxic Tooth: how a root canal could be making you sick (Nevada: Medfox Publishing, 2014), 73.

[25] Hal Huggins, "DNA Confirms Dr. Weston Price's Century-Old Findings," The Weston A. Price Foundation, posted June 25, 2010, http://www.westonaprice.org/holistic-healthcare/root-canal-dangers/.

[26] Ibid.

[27] Hal A. Huggins and Thomas E. Levy, 227.

[28] Breiner, 171.

[29] Meinig, iv.

[30] Ibid, 3.

[31] Ibid., 6.

[32] CLZ Vieira and B Caramelli, "The history of dentistry and medicine relationship: could the mouth finally return to the body?" Oral Diseases 15 (2009), 544, accessed January 4, 2016, doi:10.1111/j.1601.0825.2009.01589.x.

[33] Ibid., 1.

[34] Purinima S. Kumar, "Oral microbiota and systemic disease," Anarobe 24 (2013): 90 -93, accessed January 15, 2016, http://dx.doi.org/10.1016/j.anaerobe.2013.09.010

[35] Bill Henderson, "Root Canals and Cancer," Integrated Health Magazine, Winter 2014, 11.

[36] Hal A. Huggins and Thomas E. Levy, 205.

[37] Boyd E. Haley, Foreword to *The Toxic Tooth: How a root canal could be making you sick,* by Robert Kulacz and Thomas E. Levy (Nevada: MedFox Publishing, 2014), 17.

[38] Ibid., 16-17.

[39] Ibid., 17-18.

[40] 60 Minutes. "Is there poison in your mouth?" Filmed (December 1990). YouTube video, 22:03. Posted (October, 2012). http://www.youtube.com/watch?v=lj-51ZZpyF8.

[41] Hal A. Huggins and Thomas E. Levy, 30.

[42] Breiner, 102-104, 122. Dr. Breiner has done an excellent job presenting information about amalgam fillings. See Part II Dental Amalgams, 47-140.

[43] Caroline Hemenway, "Amalgam declared dangerous," Dentistry Today (February 10, 1989).

[44] 60 Minutes.

[45] Hal A. Huggins and Thomas E. Levy, 211.

[46] Robert Kulacz and Thomas E. Levy, *The Roots of Disease*, 126. Additional species of oral bacteria have been discovered. Aas, Jorn A. et al. "Defining the Normal Bacterial Flora of the Oral Cavity." *Journal of Clinical Microbiology* 43.11 (2005): 5721-5732. PMC. Accessed 15 Sept 2015, https://www.ncbi.nim.nih.gov/pmc/articles/PMC1287824.

[47] Johnny W. Peterson, "Bacterial Pathogenesis," in *Medical Microbiology, 4th edition,* ed. S. Baron (Texas: University of Texas Medical Branch at Galveston: 1996), chapter 7,

accessed September 15, 2015, http://www.ncbi.nlm.gov/books/NBK8526/.

[48] GPEARI. "Bacteria Mutate Much More Than Previously Thought," ScienceDaily, August 19, 2007, accessed December 29, 2015, http://www.sciencedaily.com/releases/2007/08/070818112338.htm.

[49] NIH Human Microbiome Project defines normal bacterial makeup of the body, June, 2012. Accessed December 10, 2015, http://www.genome.gov/27549144.

[50] For a full discussion on endotoxins and exotoxins, see Johnny W. Peterson, Chapter 7.

[51] S.K. Mohanty, Sunil K. Mohanty and K. Sai Leela, *Textbook of Immunology* (India: Jaypee Brothers Medical Publishers, 2014), 13.

[52] Hal A. Huggins and Thomas E. Levy, 144-145.

[53] Ibid., 259.

[54] Ibid., 241-258.

List of Figures

Fig. 7 Dentinal Tubules
Copyright: <a href='http://www.123rf.com/profile_designua'> designua / 123RF Stock Photo</a>

Fig. 8 Symptoms

Resources

Suggested Reading

Breiner, Mark A. (2011) *Whole-Body Dentistry: A Complete Guide to Understanding the Impact of Dentistry on Total Health.* Fairfield, CT: Quantum Health Press, LLC.

Huggins, Hal A. and Thomas E. Levy (1999) *Uninformed Consent: The Hidden Dangers in Dental Care.* Charlottesville, VA: Hampton Roads Publishing Company, Inc.

Huggins, Hal A. (1993) *It's All in Your Head: The Link Between Mercury Amalgams and Illness.* Garden City Park, New York: Avery Publishing Group, Inc.

Kulacz, Robert and Thomas E. Levy (2002) *The Roots of Disease: Connecting Dentistry & Medicine.* Bloomingon, IN: Xlibris Corporation.

Kulacz, Robert and Thomas E. Levy (2014) *The Toxic Tooth: How a root canal could be making you sick.* Henderson, NV: MedFox Publishing, LLC.

Meinig, George (2008) *Root Canal Cover-Up*. Ojai, CA: The Price-Pottenger Foundation, Inc.

Price, Weston A. (1923) *Dental Infection: Oral and Systemic*. Volume 1. Cleveland, OH: The Penton Publishing Company.

Price, Weston A. (1923) *Dental Infections and the Degenerative Diseases.* Volume II. Cleveland, OH: The Penton Publishing Company.

Price, Weston A. (2003) *Nutrition and Physical Degeneration.* Sixth Edition. La Mesa, CA: The Price-Pottenger Foundation, Inc.

Zeines, Victor. (2010) *Healthy Mouth, Healthy Body, The Natural Dental Program for Total Wellness.* Revised fourth Edition. Bloomingon, IN: Xlibris Corporation.

Resources

Dental materials compatibility testing:

Clifford Consulting & Research, Inc.

www.ccrlab.com

Test that identifies bacteria, fungi, viruses and parasites in dental samples:

DNA Connexions (previously Dental DNA)

www.dnaconnexions.com

System that relaxes and helps with fear and anxiety during dental surgery:

NuCalm

www.nucalm.com

<u>Other Resources</u>

Price-Pottenger Foundation

www.ppnf.org

Consumers for Dental Choice

www.toxicteeth.org

Dental Amalgam Mercury Syndrome

www.amalgam.org

International Academy of Oral Medicine and Toxicology

www.iaomt.org

International Academy of Biological Dentistry & Medicine

www.iabdm.org

About the Author

Kimberly Miles is founder of Kimberly Miles Communications, LLC, which specializes in stress management, natural health and personal growth. She has been a student of natural health, nutrition and mind-body techniques for thirty years. She earned two certifications in nutritional education from Bauman College and certifications from various organizations for mind-body techniques. In 2001, she was nominated as a WETA public radio Hometown Hero.

She received a B.A. with honors from The University of Pennsylvania and a M.A. degree from George Washington University. While an M.A. candidate, she was awarded a Smithsonian Institution Fellowship to pursue her research in American art and culture.

Kimberly authored two relaxation CDs: *The Art of Letting Go©* (2001) and *Relaxation©* (2007). Her program, *The Wholeness Principle*™, is a series of experiential courses and a retreat designed to help people dissolve chronic stress and create a more satisfying life.

She has been a popular presenter with corporate and civic audiences where she introduced the power of awareness, decision making, guided relaxation, nutrition and natural health into relevant and meaningful scenarios. She has spoken to diverse groups such as The World Bank's Spiritual Unfoldment Society, US State Department, Virginia Hospital Center at Arlington, VA and Montessori schools.

Kimberly resides in Sedona, Arizona with her husband and her dog, Mr. Wiggles. She is a proud mother of two daughters. She became passionate about natural health and healing as a result of her thirty-year quest to find the root cause of her own failing health. *At The Root* is her first book; she plans to write several more books. She enjoys hiking, gardening, cooking, spending time with her family and travel. Kimberly believes that health and well-being are our birthright.

Visit www.kimberlymiles.com

https://www.facebook.com/attherootbook
https://www.facebook.com/LivingJoyfully11
https://twitter.com/brilliantday3

Made in the USA
San Bernardino, CA
15 April 2019